Tree Planting and Aftercare

BTCV is the UK's leading practical
conservation charity. We support the activities of
more than 130,000 volunteers every year, who
take part in projects and come from all sections of
the community to do practical conservation, both
in the UK and worldwide. BTCV runs a
programme of training courses, many of which
are designed to help people put the theory
contained in the Practical Handbook series into
practice. For information about any of BTCV's
volunteering opportunities, please contact:

BTCV, 36 St Mary's Street, Wallingford,
Oxfordshire OX10 0EU.

Other titles in BTCV's
Practical Handbook series:

Dry Stone Walling

Fencing

Footpaths

Hedging

Sand Dunes

Tool Care

Waterways and Wetlands

The Urban Handbook

To order any of these, or for details of other BTCV
publications and merchandise, please contact:

BTCV Enterprises Ltd.,
Conservation Centre, Balby Road,
Doncaster DN4 0RH
Tel: 01302 572200

www.btcv.org

Tree Planting and Aftercare

a practical handbook

edited by Elizabeth Agate

Acknowledgements

In addition to those people who assisted in the compilation of
Trees and Aftercare (1991), BTCV would like to thank the following people for their
help with this revision, titled Tree Planting and Aftercare.

Joan Ackland, Trevor Benton, Neil Hutton, Suzanne Iuppa, Stephen Lees,
Pascal McCaughan, Anthony Mills, Tony Milroy,
Peter Norledge, Sonia Percival, Mike Pratt, Davina Prescott, Fran Richardson,
Andy Stokes, Paul Tarling, Andrew Taylor.

ISBN   0   946752   25   7

Edited by Elizabeth Agate

Illustrations by Linda Francis

Cover: Planting pot-grown beech at Little Wittenham Nature Reserve, Oxfordshire, photo – Rob Bowker
Tree planting to stabilise landslip on the banks of the River Tees, Co. Durham, photo – Alan Atkinson

First published as Trees and Atercare in 1991

This revised and newly illustrated edition of Tree Planting and Aftercare, first published September 2000

BTCV acknowledges support from the Department
of the Environment, Transport and the Regions.

Published by BTCV,
36 St Mary's Street, Wallingford, Oxfordshire OX10 0EU.
Telephone: 01491 821600
Registered Charity 261009

Contents

Introduction

This handbook is designed for use by conservation volunteers and others interested in planting trees.

The actual process of planting a young tree is not difficult or time consuming, although it must be done properly and with care. However, the success of planting will depend on choosing the right species for the site, and on providing an environment in which the young trees will thrive. This will require keeping the ground around the young tree weed-free, and providing protection from animals and vandals.

The temperate climate and varied soils of the British Isles allow a huge range of trees and shrubs from all over the world to be grown, and introductions of species for their fruit, timber or simply for their beauty have been made since Roman times.

When choosing trees for a particular site, you need to choose not only species which are suited to the site conditions, but those which will contribute to the wildlife value of the site, and also which will look right. In woodlands, commons, hedgerows, field edges and most other sites in rural areas, native trees should be the first choice. Preferably the plants should be of local provenance (p43), that is of a strain which is known to have long grown in the area. Clear guidelines now exist as to the natural distribution of tree and shrub species (p43). By following these guidelines you will not only be choosing species which are naturally suited to the site, but will be helping to maintain the special communities of other organisms which depend on native trees for their existence.

In existing ancient or semi-natural woodland, any planting should be avoided, and natural regeneration should be encouraged instead as a way of ensuring the continuity or expansion of the woodland.

In urban or suburban areas, in villages, school grounds, parks and gardens, trees other than native species may be appropriate. Many of our native trees grow too big for small gardens, and by using selected cultivars of native trees, or introduced species, a huge range of trees becomes available, many of which are valued for their foliage, flowers, fruit or form. The important environmental benefits of trees, which include counteracting the greenhouse effect, reducing noise and pollution, and providing shelter and shade, are shared by both native and introduced species. The higher temperatures, drier air, and increased pollution in urban areas compared to rural areas means that species from drier climates may actually thrive better than our native species, most of which are adapted to humid, cool woodland conditions.

Fruit trees have long been planted in gardens and orchards, and as well as contributing to our diet, provide the same important environmental benefits as other trees.

This handbook is mainly concerned with the planting of native trees, because of their importance in creating multi-purpose woodlands for wildlife, recreation and production of timber and wood. Many other books are available on the selection, planting and care of introduced trees for parks and gardens, and on the growing of fruit trees.

Tree planting and woodland management has been an integral part of BTCV work since its inception in 1959. Tree planting and aftercare in school grounds, community gardens, parks and other non-woodland sites is another important area of BTCV work. In the last decade it has been closely involved with the Tree Council's Tree Warden Scheme, which involves training and supporting local volunteers to take special responsibility for trees in their area. Tree nurseries are another important area of BTCV work, where support is given to volunteers in propagating trees and shrubs from locally collected seed for planting out in their local areas.

A recent important area of involvement has been the Trees of Time and Place campaign, a partnership of many environmental organisations in which BTCV has been a leading partner. The campaign encouraged individuals and groups to collect and propagate fruits and seeds from both native and introduced trees in their local area, for planting out for future generations to enjoy.

BTCV are also helping with community involvement within the 12 Community Forests in England, where the aim is to increase woodland cover to about 30% by 2030, to provide high quality environments for homes, work and leisure.

The turn of the Millennium provided an added impulse to tree planting, with the planting of Millennium Woods and other tree planting schemes throughout the country. In Gloucester for example, BTCV was instrumental to the success of the 'Trees 2000' campaign, which involved planting 2000 trees in the city, half of which were planted by community groups, local residents and other local volunteers.

1 Why plant trees?

Trees have been valued as a natural resource for thousands of years, and planting has a long history. The Romans brought many species of trees to Britain for their fruit and nuts. Orchards and garden trees were planted in the gardens of villas throughout Roman Britain (p2).

There has long been, and remains, a strong urge for a landowner to plant trees. Trees are valued for shade, shelter and privacy, for flowers and fruit and for the wildlife which they bring. Trees are valuable for fuel, building and other uses. Wherever individuals have their own land, trees usually follow. One only has to look at the way newly built, private housing will 'green' within a few years, to realise how much we like to plant trees, given the chance.

Groups, organisations, companies and local authorities may also have the same urge to improve their properties by tree planting, and in addition may be motivated by the wider environmental benefits which trees bring. These include reduction of greenhouse gases, air pollution, noise and other problems.

Planting of introduced species, and trees valued for their appearance or function has a long history. Deliberate planting of native species for timber, shelter or landscaping has a much shorter history, having started from around 1600.

Tree planting will never replace ancient woodlands, which have special ecological value due to their continuous history (see below). As a rule there should be no planting in ancient woodlands, or in those areas where natural regeneration is able to maintain or increase woodland cover (p93).

However, tree planting has great ecological benefits to complement those of the ancient and semi-natural woodlands. The leafy suburbs, urban parks and roadside plantings, and the natural colonisation of undeveloped urban land are together creating a mosaic of habitats to rival those of the 'countryside'. So much rural land has become an ecological wasteland due to intensive agriculture, the removal or neglect of hedges, and the destruction or over-grazing of woodlands, that the creation of new woodland habitats by planting, natural regeneration and colonisation has become of great importance. Many woodland birds, for example, are now more numerous in the suburbs than they are in the countryside. Garden and street trees, shrubs and lawns reproduce the varied structure and cover of natural woodland, and for birds, the variety of non-native species is a bonus, providing extra food sources.

The history of woodlands

The history of woodlands in Britain is a history of woodland clearance and management. Historical evidence suggests that there was as little woodland cover in Roman times as there is today. The Romans, invading England in AD43, found a land where agriculture was fully developed, and the river flood-plains and chalklands had long been cleared of the original wildwood. The Romans were an urban and industrial people, and required large quantities of timber for building, and wood for fuel, both for domestic use and for industrial uses such as ironworking. Woodlands were highly managed.

With the retreat of the Roman Empire and the coming of the Dark Ages there was a collapse in industrial activity, communications, and a huge reduction in population. The main effect was in the towns and other settlements, many of which were abandoned. It appears that there was not a great expansion of secondary woodland on abandoned farmland, but that rural activity continued, even if at a reduced level. Woodlands were still vital for the provision of domestic fuel and building materials.

Woodlands were managed mainly by coppicing. Coppicing is a way of harvesting a tree by cutting it down to ground level at regular intervals, at a stage when the growth can easily be cut by hand tools. The cut poles can be used for fuel, building, tools, baskets and many other purposes. The tree regrows from the stump or stool, so that a crop can be taken from a woodland for many years without the need for any replanting. This was in the past, and remains, a very efficient way of producing wood. From an ecological point of view, it means that the rootstock of each stool may be

One year regrowth of hazel coppice

directly related to the trees of the ancient wildwood, giving a link to the genetic stock of thousands of years ago. The woodland soil and ground flora also remains undisturbed, giving continuity with the past, and ensuring the health of the woodland ecosystem for the future.

Coppicing has been carried out since Neolithic times. The produce of coppicing was, in the past, far more important than the large timber produced from cutting down mature trees, which was used only for large beams, gateposts, planks and for shipbuilding. The smaller material, called wood, was legally anything less than 2 foot in girth. It was produced from coppicing, and from the branches of trees felled for timber, and was the mainstay of the rural economy.

Pollarding is a similar ancient technique, used to produce a regular supply of wood by cutting the tree back 1.8m (6') or more above the ground, to produce growth out of the reach of grazing animals. This method of management creates a 'wood pasture', with grassland for grazing animals and scattered pollarded trees, and was widely used in the past. It may link back to an ancient 'savanna' type vegetation cover in Britain, created by herds of grazing wild animals, and is possibly more 'natural' than dense woodland.

About one-sixth of the original woodland probably remained at the time of the Domesday Book, in 1086. This woodland remained mainly under traditional coppice management for nearly another thousand years, with only a small decrease in area. From 1945 came a great change. The destruction that took place was not a matter of felling trees which would grow again, as had happened in the past, but mainly of converting ancient woodland sites to other uses. Rackham (1990) estimates that one half of the remaining ancient woodland was converted, mainly to conifer plantations, followed by agriculture. Housing, roads, industry and quarrying accounted for only a small amount. However, afforestation with conifers in some cases merely suppressed the natural woodland, which is now recovering (p3).

The history of tree planting

ORCHARD AND GARDEN TREES

The skill of tree planting has been around for a very long time. The ancient civilisations had gardens and orchards into which they transplanted trees that bore useful crops, or those that could be clipped into hedges, or those which were valued for their shade or beauty. Trees were not only transplanted from the immediate area of natural woodland, but were collected and traded over great distances.

The ancient Greeks and Romans were great planters. The Romans have left evidence in their extensive horticultural manuals of how they planted trees. Advice included avoiding damage to roots, digging a large enough hole, and marking a tree with red ochre on one side before it was dug up, so that it could be replanted with the same orientation to sun and wind. There was also emphasis on not leaving tree roots exposed to the air. Baskets were used for transplanting, and for 'container growing'.

The Romans brought to Britain the cultivated apple, the black mulberry, the fig, the sweet chestnut, the common walnut and the medlar. The Romans were skilled gardeners and growers, and had a special name, the arborator, for a tree-tender. The ornamental gardener was called the topiarius; he tended evergreen trees and shrubs and was expert at topiary, which became a major passion of the Romans. The native box, holly and ivy, along with introduced laurel, cypress and myrtle, were used for edging ornamental beds in courtyards near the house. The Romans also made elaborate tree seats and tree houses (Huxley, 1978).

Planting of fruit, nut and ornamental trees in gardens continued in times of peace and prosperity. Once towns and settlements no longer needed to be crowded behind fortifications, space became available for gardens and planting. The Domesday Book (1086) mentions both horti (gardens) and hortuli (little gardens) in number. Monastery gardens were the most complex, with orchards of fruit and nut trees and large vegetable gardens. By the reign of Henry II (1154-1189) the wealthy citizens of London had relatively large gardens attached to their houses.

The practice of undercutting or transplanting in the nursery to produce a mass of fibrous roots which would aid establishment was recommended as early as 1569, by Dutch writers. Special tools for transplanting were developed, including split tubes of metal, which were pushed into the ground around a young plant.

As the prosperity of the great landowners increased from the early 16th century, planting of trees on a large scale for ornamental effect began.

In 1664, the diarist, statesman, gardener and arboriculturist

John Evelyn published *Sylva, A Discourse of Forest Trees*, which included details of the propagation, planting and maintenance of native trees. Extensive planting of avenues and plantations by wealthy landowners had started as early as the 1500s, and John Evelyn had learnt much from travelling widely in Britain and abroad. *Sylva* influenced more planting by landowners, including King Charles II, who ordered a large amount of planting in the New Forest and the Forest of Dean, to provide timber for shipbuilding.

By the mid 18th century, Capability Brown and others were sweeping away many of the earlier formal designs, instead planting in curves and clumps to create the English landscape garden. Large trees were often moved, using various contraptions invented for the purpose. As was noted by a writer early in the 19th century, 'such Trees, for several years, grow so slowly, as to remind one of stricken deer' (quoted in Huxley, 1978).

PLANTING FOR TIMBER

The 'plantation movement', which began around 1600 and continued well into the 1800s, was characterised by experimentation with species choice, mostly for practical reasons. Oak, ash, beech, elm and sweet chestnut were planted for the purpose of producing items ranging from ships' keels to coffins.

Much new planting took place in Scotland, where by the beginning of the 18th century it had become a fashionable hobby. Scots pine was the favoured species, although European Larch also became popular towards the end of the century. In England and Wales, landowners produced timber by supplementary planting in coppice woodlands, or by extending existing parks and woods, as new sites for afforestation were fewer than in Scotland. Oak and beech, with Scots pine as a 'nurse', were widely used.

Many of these plantations in England and Wales were never harvested, because of the changes brought about during the 19th century. Huge imports of cheap timber from other countries then under British rule made private domestic planting for timber production unprofitable. Stands of oak planted during the plantation movement were unsaleable, and their remains comprise much of today's 'traditional woodlands'.

Private planting had nearly ceased by the end of the 19th century, and did not start again until the 1950s. By the start of the 20th century, Britain was almost totally reliant on imported timber and forestry products. The heavy demands and the reduction of imports brought about by the First World War led to severe shortages of timber, and about 180,000 hectares (450,000 acres) of privately owned woodlands were felled to meet the demand.

In 1919 the Forestry Commission was established to ensure such a situation could not arise again, and began a massive planting campaign. Using mostly conifers and other fast-growing species, about 145,000 hectares (359,000 acres) were planted. Single species or simple mixtures in straight lines were planted close together in large, even-aged blocks, and laid out with little consideration for landscape variations. Much of this planting was on heathland and moorland, damaging or destroying their fragile ecology.

When the Second World War began, the Commission plantations were too young to harvest, and a second major felling of about 212,000 hectares (524,000 acres) of private woodland was necessary.

However felling is not necessarily a problem for the continuity of woodlands. Trees regrow from felled stumps, from suckers and from seed. As long as the ground is not cleared by machine, or turned over to another use, the woodland will regrow. It may have a different structure, and have different proportions of species, but it will still have features of the earlier wood.

More damaging was the period from 1945 to about 1975. Food shortages during the Second World War led to a policy of increasing agricultural production and efficiency. Many woods, copses and hedgerows were removed to increase the area under cultivation, and to make field sizes larger and more suitable for modern machinery.

Grants also encouraged the planting of conifers in ancient and other woodlands, to increase timber production, and during the period from 1945 this was the major cause of damage to ancient woodlands. However by the end of the 20th century, the situation for ancient woodlands appeared much less bleak. In many of these plantations the original trees had regrown, and suppressed the planted conifers (Rackham, 1990). The Forestry Commission now recognises an important category of woodland called Plantations on Ancient Woodland Sites, and advice is directed at their restoration.

Planting of introduced species on heathland and moorland has virtually ceased. Many of the plantations made between and after the wars have reached maturity, and are being felled. Management is being directed much more at multi-use forests, where recreation and wildlife have a high priority. Ironically, some of these plantations have become well-loved features in the landscape, and their removal to restore heathland can be a cause of public outcry.

In Scotland, recent surveys have shown that the native woodland resource of Scotland is greater than had earlier been estimated, and that a considerable amount of new native woodlands are being created. The current estimate of native woodland is 320,938 hectares (792,717 acres), of which 47% is natural origin, and 53% planted origin native woodlands (MacKenzie, Forestry Commission, 1999).

The Forestry Commission have also recently moved away from their general policy of managing broadleaved, coniferous and mixed woodland by clear felling. Instead more natural 'continuous cover' systems are being developed, under which there is selective felling of trees within a woodland, and natural regeneration and replanting are used to maintain a continuous woodland cover. Clear felling and replanting is an expensive operation, in terms of labour and resources. It can also be highly damaging to soils, drainage and ecological systems within the woodland, so that essentially each time a wood is clear-felled, its value as a capital resource is destroyed. Continuous cover forestry requires greater skill to manage successfully, and involves working with the woodland in a much more natural way.

THE GREENING OF CITIES

Ebenezer Howard's *Garden Cities of Tomorrow* (1898) inspired a new approach to solving the urban crisis. He advocated the building of planned towns incorporating low-density housing with trees and green spaces. Letchworth and Welwyn Garden City, now richly endowed

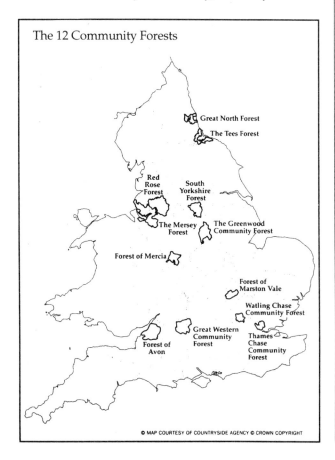

The 12 Community Forests

Great North Forest
The Tees Forest
Red Rose Forest
South Yorkshire Forest
The Mersey Forest
The Greenwood Community Forest
Forest of Mercia
Forest of Marston Vale
Watling Chase Community Forest
Great Western Community Forest
Forest of Avon
Thames Chase Community Forest

© MAP COURTESY OF COUNTRYSIDE AGENCY © CROWN COPYRIGHT

with trees, were built to his design. Howard's ideas also gave impetus to the establishment of New Towns, 28 of which were designated from 1946, and which have had a high success rate, in both commercial and amenity terms, with their urban forestry schemes. In the older cities, development mainly persisted with no overall landscaping plan to balance it. While some trees and woodlands survived to form part of the urban expansion, many were felled to make way for roads and other building schemes.

The desire to improve urban areas by 'greening' them persisted, and by the 1970s, urban ecology had become a distinct discipline, with great interest in conserving, planting and managing many urban green spaces. Much of this work is being continued through the implementation of the Community Forests (see below).

Government agencies, non-governmental organisations, charities, local authorities, highway authorities, service providers and many other groups are involved directly or indirectly in tree planting. The Countryside Agency is working to double the area of woodland in England, with similar targets set by the agencies in Wales, Scotland and Northern Ireland.

THE COMMUNITY FORESTS

The 12 Community Forests in England were started in the early 1990s through a partnership between the Countryside Agency, the Forestry Commission, local authorities, businesses and voluntary groups. The Community Forest initiative has multiple aims:

- An increase in woodland coverage. Only 7% of England is wooded, which is the second lowest percentage in the European Union. In each Forest, the aim is to plant up to 30% of the area, to create a wooded framework for multiple use.

- To encourage economic regeneration, by providing high quality environments in which people can live, work and relax.

- Managing new and existing woodland to encourage enterprise, jobs and training.

- Maintaining and creating new habitats, not only of woodland, but also glades, meadows, hedgerows, ponds, wetlands and other areas for wildlife and people.

- Improvement of access for walkers, cyclists, canoeists and other recreation users. Where possible, routes are linked to the National Cycle Network, National Trails, Greenways and to public transport provision.

- Providing opportunities for school groups and others to use the forest for learning, creative activities and other projects.

- Community participation, not only in practical management but also in initiating many types of creative art and community projects within the Forest.

- Reclamation of derelict land and landfill sites by tree planting and other environmental improvements.

In each Forest, a locally based team works with agencies, landowners, farmers, businesses and local communities to implement the plan agreed by local people and Government. Some projects involve a change of land ownership, but most land remains in its original ownership, but managed in a different way.

It is planned that the Community Forest programme will last until at least 2030. In the period 1991-1999, 6,220 hectares (15,370 acres) of new woodland were planted, and 8,796 hectares (21,735 acres) of existing woodland were brought into management. About 10,112 hectares (24,987 acres) of woodland were opened up for access and recreation. In addition, there was creation or improvement of access routes, hedgerows and other habitats. Further details are available in *Regeneration around cities* (Countryside Agency, 1999).

The benefits of trees

This section gives a brief outline of the main benefits of trees and woodland.

CLIMATE CHANGE

The capability of trees to affect climate through the cycling of CO_2 is becoming ever more important because of the connection with global warming.

Satellite studies made in 1999 have shown how the spread of mega-cities around the world has created vast 'heat islands', that cause smog, trigger thunderstorms and reduce the productivity of the land. In America, Atlanta has lost on average 55 acres of trees every day for two decades. The hard surfaces of the city soak up radiant energy during the day, and hold on to it at night. Consequently more energy is needed for air conditioning, creating more ozone and smog. The heat at night creates a low pressure system, with hot air rising and cooler surrounding air rushing in to replace it, so increasing the number of storms. Tree planting is one of the ways of reducing this heat island effect, but the scale of planting needed is massive. In China's Pearl River delta the urban sprawl grew by 319% between 1988 and 1996. The need to plant trees and restore woodland cover in many parts of the world is urgent.

Trees directly affect climate and air quality in many ways; by oxygenating, humidifying, modifying temperature and wind patterns, and metabolizing pollution. Even smaller groupings of some species can be useful as oxygenators.

The foliage of a single mature beech tree, for example, can extract more than 2.5kg (5.5lb) of CO_2 from the atmosphere, and produce 1.7kg (3.7lb) of oxygen in one hour, which in theory is enough for the needs of ten people in a year. Depending partly on leaf size, trees can also transpire large amounts of water, a process which cools and humidifies the surrounding air. A mature beech can transpire up to 440 litres (100 gallons) of water a day. Planted in a green network around and within built-up areas, trees work in several ways. They cool the air through transpiration, control the heat which radiates from roads and buildings, and disperse the warm, polluted air that tends to hover over inner cities.

Belts of trees filtering dust and pollution

Trees can help reduce the damage done by air pollutants and vehicle emissions through creating air turbulence. 'Woodland edge' plantings of shrubby species are particularly suited to this purpose. Pollutants can also be filtered and to some extent absorbed by the foliage of trees. Dust is easily filtered out from the atmosphere, becoming trapped on the leaves of trees and then washed down by rain.

WILDLIFE

The complex nature of native semi-natural woodlands in Britain is the result of long evolution and human interference. A newly planted woodland will take many decades before it begins to develop the wide range of dependent flora and fauna of a long established wood. To best encourage both immediate benefits for wildlife, and the gradual ingress of other species, many factors will need to be taken into account. These include the soils, location, most suitable species, planting layout and maintenance procedures.

Woodlands with a varied structure, with trees of different size, shape and stage of maturity will greatly increase the diversity of a woodland, and encourage more species. The number of bird species in a woodland, for example, is related much less to the variety of tree species than to a varied structure, which offers more opportunities for breeding, nesting and feeding. Woods with a limited structural variety can be improved for wildlife by introducing diversity in the number and types of woodland layers.

Different tree species create microclimates which influence what grows beneath them. They do this by controlling the amount of moisture and wind reaching the lower layers, the light intensity at ground level, the organic composition of the leaf litter in the soil, and the uptake of soil moisture and nutrients. The trees you plant will therefore influence the species which colonise in the layers beneath. The local seed zones (p43) set out which species may be appropriate in different parts of the country, according to their natural distribution.

NOISE REDUCTION

Excessive noise from traffic or other sources is a form of environmental pollution, and trees can be useful in lessening it to some degree. The leaves of a tree tend to scatter sound, and its trunk to reflect it. Trees with dense foliage and large leaves, such as plane or large-leaved lime, are the best choice. Woodland plantings are even more effective, as the soft surface created by leaf fall, deadwood and ground cover tends to absorb sound. Where there is only room for a belt of planting, this should be 8-12m (27-30') in width, with a thick understorey on either side. The belt should reach a height of at least 5m (16') in the middle.

SHELTER

Clumps or belts of trees and tall hedges have been planted as windbreaks on farmland for many centuries to shield crops, buildings and livestock from exposure. Open spaces such as playing fields, parks, urban squares and industrial sites can be improved by the planting of strategic shelterbelts.

Trees reduce the force of the wind and modify its movement around buildings. Factors influencing the effectiveness of windbreaks and shelterbelts include the dimensions of the group of trees and the planting density. Very dense barriers are counterproductive, and some permeability is necessary. Shelterbelts around buildings can reduce fuel consumption in winter, and provide shade in summer. For further details on shelterbelts see page 27.

LANDSCAPE, AMENITY AND RECREATION

Trees, in woodlands, hedgerows, roadsides, parks, gardens and all types of location are a vital part of our landscape, in rural and urban areas. Some are remnants of semi-natural woodland, but many are planted, and the beauty of many wooded landscapes is due to tree planters of previous centuries.

Trees provide the backdrop for many urban views, and soften and disguise the harsh outlines of buildings and roads.

Wooded landscapes, commons, parks and places with scattered trees are favourite places for walking, picnicking and other forms of recreation.

Where not to plant trees

ANCIENT AND SEMI-NATURAL WOODLANDS

The lesson has been learnt that ancient woodlands are too valuable a natural resource to suffer interference. Management in the main is limited to the coppicing and occasional selective felling which ensured the survival of these woodlands for so many thousands of years.

Many newer woodlands, also, need sensitive management where natural regeneration is used instead of planting as a way of restocking the wood. See page 93.

CHANGING LAND USES

Left unused, nearly all land below 800m (2,000ft) in Britain would eventually be tree-covered. Natural colonisation usually takes over where agriculture or development has retreated. Blackthorn and other species tend to spread from hedges and copses into unused agricultural land.

Disused industrial sites, old railways and derelict land become grown over with pioneer species such as birch and alder. Many of these sites have highly altered substrates, with free-draining industrial waste or rubble contrasting with pools, marshes and heavily compacted waterlogged ground. Some of these sites have, with little management, become highly valuable wildlife sites, with their locations in urban and industrial areas making them green oases in otherwise built-up areas. Management may be needed to improve access, to diversify or enhance habitats, but in general it's better to work with the natural regeneration rather than undertake extensive replanting.

STORM DAMAGE

The storms of 1987 and 1990 caused a swathe of damage across southern England. The 1987 storm blew down 15 million trees, of which 12 million were forest trees, and 3 million were individual trees in parks, gardens and street. In the last days of the 20th century a hurricane swept across France and blew down an estimated 360 million trees.

Certainly the 1987 storm was most damaging to man-made woodlands. Plantations, planted parkland and street trees suffered very badly. Ancient woodlands, semi-natural mixed woodlands and even ancient natural trees in parkland suffered much less. The storm in France completely devastated many 18th century Royal Parks, in which many of the trees were planted as mature specimens to create instant landscapes. Monocultures of similar-aged trees have been flattened.

Clear evidence of the 1987 and 1990 storms, and immediate observations from the 1999 storm is that naturally regenerated trees suffer very much less from storms that do planted trees. In the 1987 storm, about 30% of coniferous woodland in East Sussex suffered severe (more than 50%) damage, with broadleaved woodland suffering only about 7% severe damage. The least damage was to free-standing trees accustomed to exposure, and to woodland edge trees. However, where even the woodland edge trees had fallen, particularly around large woods, the trees within the woodland were mostly flattened. Small woods and clumps of less than an acre tended to fare better (*Tree News*, 1998).

In the rush to restore damage after the 1987 storm, some woodlands were damaged by the process of extracting timber and replanting. Those woodlands which were left to recover naturally have fared better. Obviously access routes have to be cleared and dangerous trees removed, but in general it is better to intervene as little as possible. Trees naturally fall or lose branches. Some fallen trees will continue to grow in a prone position. Broken trees regrow

like a pollard. Other trees will regenerate from the stump or rootstock, so that the genetic strain lives on. New trees will generate from seed in the openings in the canopy where trees have fallen. Fallen dead wood has great ecological value and contributes to the overall health of the woodland ecosystem.

Tree continuing to grow from prone position

Mixed age woodlands, managed as necessary by a system of continuous cover forestry, are not only the best for wildlife, and economically sound, but also the best insurance against storm damage.

The storms also taught a lesson about planting. Trees must be planted very young, as small transplants. This gives them the best chance of growing the type of root structure and shape of trunk which will allow them to withstand storms. Although natural regeneration and continuous cover forestry are the best way to manage woodlands and forests, there is still the desire and need to plant new woodlands, and to plant avenues and clumps of trees, individual street trees and other ornamental plantings. For the best chance of long life, these trees must be planted small. It's also essential to choose species that are suited to the site. The storms exposed the shallow, insufficient root structures of many trees planted in the wrong type of soil or situation.

2 Planning and design

This chapter looks at the planning and design of woodlands for multi-purpose uses, which might include landscape improvement, wildlife, recreation, community involvement, and production of timber or coppice material. Planting of small groups of trees, avenues and individual trees is also considered. The information concentrates on native species, but introduced species may also be appropriate.

Site assessment

Before you begin planning, you should ask the following questions:

SHOULD TREES BE PLANTED AT ALL?

- Who owns the site? Will the owner give permission for planting?

- What is the site used for? Will planting affect this use?

- Will trees block views or deprive any nearby houses of sunlight?

- Is the site already an interesting wildlife habitat? Old grassland, heathland, bogs or damp ground may be more valuable as they are. Scrub is an important habitat, and is not necessarily improved by being converted to woodland.

- Are trees already growing on the site? If young trees are colonising the site, or existing sparse woodland cover is regenerating, it shouldn't be necessary to plant trees (p6). Trees should not be planted in ancient or semi-natural woodlands (p6).

- Tree roots can damage archaeological remains, as well as obscure surface evidence.

- Will the trees you plant have a secure future? Trees must not be planted if aftercare cannot be guaranteed for at least the next five years. On sites where ownership or land use may change, tree planting may not be a worthwhile investment.

- There may be a good reason for the site being treeless. The soil may be too thin or polluted; the site may be too exposed, waterlogged or overgrazed.

HOW THE SITE AFFECTS THE CHOICE OF SPECIES

- Where the aim is to try and recreate semi-natural woodland cover, species local to the area should be chosen. Not only should the species be local, but the planting stock should be of local provenance, meaning it is derived from trees which have long grown in the area (p43). Knowledge and observation of existing local woods will assist in choosing species and designing the type of woodland appropriate to the area.

- Check the soil conditions. Soils naturally vary, sometimes in quite a small area, and disturbance of the soil by building development, industry, agriculture and other factors may have affected it. Species must match the local site conditions (Table 2d, p21).

- Is the site very exposed to the wind? Is it near the coast, where salt winds will affect growth?

- Consider the eventual height of trees in relation to the available space. Native forest species may be too big to grow near buildings, and other species should be chosen. The vigour of the root system and its effect on buildings and underground services must also be considered (p29).

- Is it appropriate to use non-native trees? In streets, gardens and parks where landscape value may have priority, non-native species will greatly add to the range of trees which can be planted, and may have characteristics which make them more suitable than native trees. Many have flowers, bark, autumn colour and other features which are a great attraction, and fruit trees are always valued. In urban situations, introduced trees may be better than no trees.

- In creating woodland on exposed sites or polluted soils, non-native species may be needed to establish shelter or woodland cover, to which the native species are added.

PLANTING AREA

This section gives a guide to the type of planting which is generally appropriate for small to medium sites.

Non-woodland planting

These include small groups of trees, narrow shelterbelts, avenues, orchards and individual trees.

Less than .25 hectare

These include small areas of planting and clumps of trees for screening, shelter and landscape value. Such areas have a limited potential to develop the full range of woodland structure, but can still be valuable for wildlife, play and education. School wildlife gardens can incorporate a range of woodland and other habitats which have high educational value. Small areas of planting may qualify for grants from the local authority or other sources, but do not qualify for the Woodland Grant Scheme, for which the minimum area is usually .25 hectare.

Up to 1 hectare

Woods of up to 1 hectare can be a valuable landscape feature on a local scale. They can become an interesting wildlife habitat, and if near housing are valuable for children's play. A hectare of woodland can have paths under the canopy, but in the mature woodland, there will not be sufficient space for open glades or wide paths with grassy edges. Although a mixture of understorey shrubs and trees can be included, it may be best to limit the tallest trees to two or three species, in order to produce a woodland of a particular character (see below).

Up to 3 hectares

Woods of this size can be divided into different types, differentiated by the species mix or type of woodland structure, including areas of coppice. Glades and open areas can be incorporated within the wood, linked by paths. A woodland area of 3 hectares can be a significant feature for local residents, providing space for recreation, dog-walking and other uses.

Over 3 hectares

These are major projects, usually involving several agencies. Work may include tree planting, management of existing woodland, habitat improvement, provision of car parks and other facilities. Production of commercial timber may be included as part of the woodland management scheme.

Woodland structure

For recreation and visual value, the structure of the woodland tends to be more important than the particular species. For recreation use, most people like a woodland which is fairly open and light, with tall, clear stemmed or spreading, branched trees that you can see between, and with little undergrowth. This type of woodland may be highly managed, and may consist entirely of planted trees. A woodland which approaches more natural conditions, with a varied structure, an understorey, thickets of natural regeneration, fallen timber and trees of varying shapes and sizes, may not be

so attractive to many people. Children, though, love bushes for dens, narrow paths for creeping through, low branches for swinging and climbing, muddy banks for sliding and plenty of interest at their level.

Open woodlands, which are attractive for recreation, can be vulnerable to storm damage. They may also be too draughty and exposed to be of much value for wildlife. Dense growth around the edges of woodland, which gives shelter to the habitat within, may not be popular with woodland users, who can be afraid of losing their way, or of being attacked (p25).

Much of the worst damage in the storms of 1987 and 1990 was to plantations, and to planted trees (p6).

In creating new woodlands, the challenge is to use local species in a way which fulfils the expectations and desires of users, whilst also creating a woodland which is ecologically diverse and resistant to storm damage.

TYPES OF STRUCTURE

Described below and overleaf are types of woodland structure, which relate to the way trees are managed. In planning a woodland, you need to decide on the type of structure most suitable to the purpose of the woodland. The type of structure affects the choice of species, spacing and early management.

High forest

In high forest, trees are allowed to grow to their mature height. The trees may be even aged, as in a plantation, or may be of mixed ages. Newly planted woodland will need thinning and possibly pruning to create a high forest system. Mature high forest is attractive for recreation use, as the trees are well spaced and the canopy is high.

Coppice

Coppice is produced by cutting near the base of the stem or trunk, which results in the cut stump producing many shoots. Coppicing is an ancient technique used to produce wood which could be easily cut with simple hand tools, and which had many uses. Coppiced woodland is very valuable for wildlife, especially flowers and butterflies, because of the changing conditions of light during the coppice rotation. The area of coppice, called a coupe, needs to be at least 0.1ha (c.30m x 30m) in area to develop properly, or 0.5 ha for commercial coppicing. Too small an area within a woodland will be shaded by surrounding trees and will not produce strong regrowth. Coppice is valuable for recreation in the later part of the rotation, and is ideal for involving local people in active management. All native broadleaved species can be coppiced, although the products of some species are of higher commercial value than others.

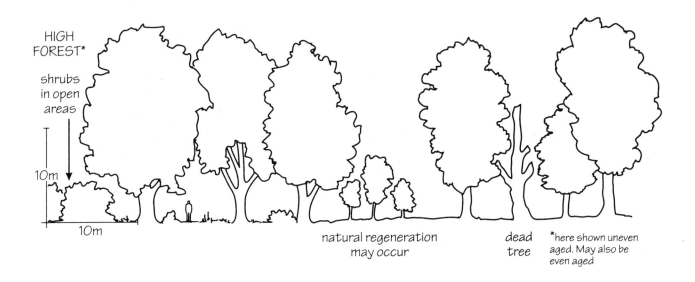

HIGH
FOREST*

shrubs
in open
areas

10m

10m

natural regeneration
may occur

dead
tree

*here shown uneven
aged. May also be
even aged

COPPICE

10m

10m

newly cut, showing first year growth

mature

COPPICE WITH STANDARDS

10m

10m

Continued...

Coppice with standards

This is a two-storey forest, with scattered standard trees above an understorey of coppice. The coppice is cut on a short rotation for fuel, fencing and other purposes, and the standards are grown on a longer rotation and felled for timber as they mature. This silviculture system was widely used in the past, and was the legally required method of managing woodlands in the time of Henry VIII (1509-47), when at least 30 standards per hectare had to be grown. With the exception of hazel, which only grows as a multi-stemmed shrub, standards can be the same species as the coppice layer, although beech is unsuitable as a standard because of the heavy shade it casts. Oak is the most common standard species. Coppice with standards requires careful long-term management, and felling can appear destructive. For amenity woodlands it is usually better to intermix areas of high forest with areas of coppice, rather than to use the coppice with standards system.

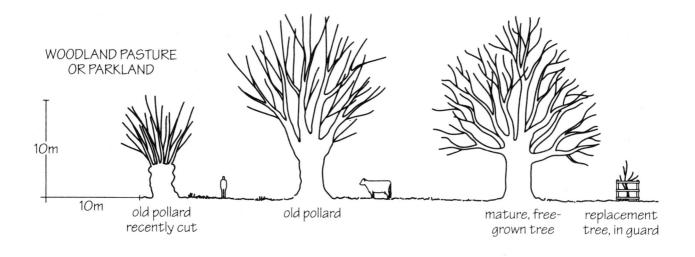

WOODLAND PASTURE OR PARKLAND

10m

10m

old pollard recently cut   old pollard   mature, free-grown tree   replacement tree, in guard

SPINNEYS   WOODLAND EDGES

10m

10m   shrubs, scrub and small trees

Wood pasture or parkland

Wood pasture is a system of land-use which combines trees with pasture for grazing animals. Some of the trees are pollarded, which means they are periodically cut at 2-3m above ground level. Growth sprouts in the same way as from a tree coppiced at ground level, except that the new shoots are out of reach of browsing animals. Pollards are harvested for firewood, fencing, building and other uses. Pollarding renews the tree in the same way as coppicing, and pollarded trees are amongst the oldest trees in Britain.

Wood pasture is an ancient system of management, in use from the middle ages. The landscape it produces may also have very ancient roots, as recent theories suggest that parts of post-glacial Britain may have had a savanna-type landscape of grass with scattered trees, which would have resulted from the grazing of large herds of animals. Over the centuries, an idealised landscape of trees and grass has been recreated in deer parks, landscape gardens, urban parks, golf courses and arboreta. Although not as diverse as woodland, scattered trees can have great wildlife value, and can be seen and appreciated in a way that is not always possible with trees in woodland. Many people who find dense woodland threatening will not fail to be drawn by a landscape of scattered trees and grass.

Wood pastures, wooded commons and parks grazed by stock still exist, and contain some of Britain's most ancient trees, together with unique assemblages of lichens and other organisms. At low grazing densities, trees can regenerate without protection. At higher grazing densities, fencing will be needed to protect natural regeneration. See

Rackham (1990) for details on the history of wood pastures and wooded commons, and Read (2000) for details on the management of veteran trees.

Many important landscape parks were created by tree planting, which has continued over the generations to replace and extend areas of parkland. Introduced species were often used, and were the *raison d'être* of arboreta, or collections of trees.

Woodland edges, spinneys and scrub

Woodland edges may be characterised by species of trees and shrubs which are different to those within the woodland. The light and space also allows more spreading, bushy growth, with lower branching, compared to trees in woodland. In some cases, edges have been created by planting species which provide shelter for the woodland within (p16). In other cases, the characteristic edge evolves naturally from those species which are light demanding or colonising. Grazing around woodlands tends to leave an edge of hawthorn, blackthorn, elder and other unpalatable species. Some plantations had hedges planted around them, which may remain as fully grown hawthorn or other hedging species. Woodland edges are very important for wildlife, both because of their structure and variety, but also because of the particular plant species they contain. Many invertebrates, birds, small mammals and reptiles rely on woodland edge or scrub habitat.

Small areas of woodland edge habitat can be created by planting hedges and clumps of hedging species or 'scrub'. Traditionally 'spinneys' are small areas of woodland, mainly comprising spiny species such as hawthorn or blackthorn. This type of planting is useful for screening, shelter, protecting vulnerable habitats and limiting access. Depending on the situation, it may develop into woodland if taller tree species seed into it. Exposed sites, very poor soils or other limiting factors may keep scrub as the climax vegetation.

CREATING STRUCTURE

Structure is a function of the species selected, the spacing at planting, and the way that the trees are thinned, pruned or coppiced in the years after planting. This is too complex a subject to deal with in detail in this handbook. For further information refer to *Creating and Managing Woodlands around Towns* (Forestry Commission Handbook 11, 1995), *Creating New Native Woodlands* (Forestry Commission Bulletin 112, 1994) and *Silviculture of Broadleaved Woodland* (Forestry Commission Bulletin 62, 1984).

The general formula for establishing trees, either in small groups or to create large areas of new woodland, is to plant trees small and close together, spaced 2 or 3m apart. This quickly produces a woodland-type environment or thicket, where shade and shelter mutually benefits the trees, and the ground quickly becomes too shady for grass to grow. The beneficial effects extend underground, where mycorrhizal activity (p70) which greatly enhances tree growth is more likely to establish than under grass. The trees must then be successively thinned to leave the 'final crop' trees. (This standard terminology is used here to describe those trees which are planned to be grown through to maturity, and which are the main object of the design.

In commercial woodland they will be a 'crop', but in amenity or conservation woodland they may never be felled for timber).

As explained below, you may thus plant anywhere between 9 and 40 young trees for every tree you want to grow to maturity. At planting this may seem very wasteful, but this system has many advantages both in the way it encourages

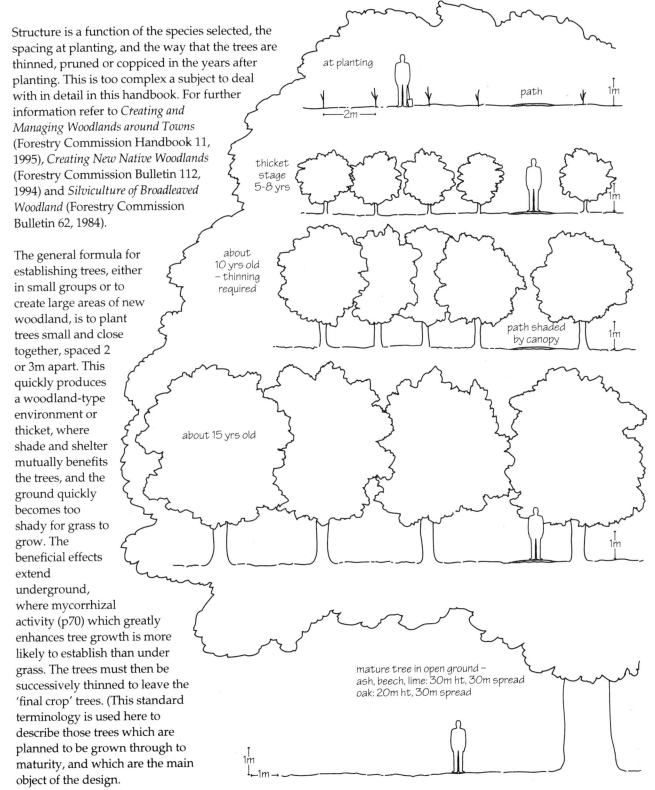

at planting

path   1m

2m

thicket stage 5-8 yrs

1m

about 10 yrs old – thinning required

path shaded by canopy   1m

about 15 yrs old

1m

mature tree in open ground – ash, beech, lime: 30m ht, 30m spread oak: 20m ht, 30m spread

1m

1m

trees to grow, and in related management. By planting densely, you are creating an environment in which the trees can flourish. The most important factor in establishing trees is keeping them weed-free, and especially grass-free (p97). If you plant close and weed properly, within four or five years grass and other weed growth will have been suppressed, the trees will be well established and thinning can be started to select the final trees. The thicket of growth has the advantage of keeping people and mowers away, both of which can be damaging. The thicket stage may not be popular with local people, and the system needs explaining where planting is close to housing or public access areas. A thicket looks untidy, and you can't see through it. It should be explained, for example, that what appears a jumble of growth is nurturing the four or five trees which will emerge to form the intended design. If you just plant five trees in grass, the planting is likely to be unsuccessful.

High forest

In a natural woodland, there is not a great mixture of species, but usually two or three dominant overstorey or forest trees, and two or three frequently occurring understorey species. This is the best pattern to follow when creating new woodlands, because it mimics a natural woodland and is thus likely to be the most simple and successful to establish. Soil and other conditions naturally limit the number of species, and it is not a good idea to add more just for variety. The planting of rare native species should not be generally encouraged, because part of their attraction is their rarity. Details on species are given in the next section.

The generally accepted method is to plant in groups of 9, 16 or 25 of each species. The trees in each group are then successively thinned to leave one tree which grows to maturity. These groups can be arranged in a particular pattern, or can be arranged randomly. For timber production, the final crop trees need to be evenly spaced to optimise growth. In amenity woodlands, a pattern which results in unevenly spaced final crop trees is usually preferred. The pattern must relate to the proportion of species which have been chosen.

A simplified example, which can also be used as a 'rule of thumb', is shown below. This uses three species in equal proportions, with the groups randomly arranged. The trees are planted 3.3m apart, or 9 trees to a 10m x 10m square, which is equivalent to 900 trees per hectare. The trees are thinned every 5-10 years over about 40 years (p110), to leave one tree from each group of nine. The mature woodland thus has trees spaced on average 10 m apart, at a total of 100 trees per hectare. (This planting rate approximates to the Woodland Grant Scheme rate for amenity woodlands below 3 hectares, which is 1100 per hectare or a 3m spacing. See page 116).

This simplified example uses three species in equal proportions, planted on the square in a square hectare. Variation can be introduced into the planting design in many ways:

- Nurse species may be included, for example fast growing or nitrogen fixing species, to aid the growth of slower growing more desirable trees. These should be removed once their purpose has been fulfilled.

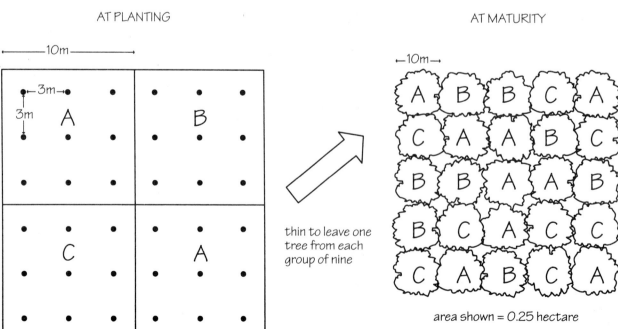

Three species (A, B, & C) in equal proportion, in groups of nine; groups arranged randomly

AT PLANTING AT MATURITY

thin to leave one tree from each group of nine

area shown = 0.25 hectare

- Understorey species may be included, which will be naturally suppressed as the canopy grows up.

- Choice of species must follow physical variations within the site, for example soil type.

- Groups can be varied in shape or size, while keeping to the basic plant spacing. Planting in irregular 'drifts' which follow land form and contour gives a more natural effect.

- Glades, rides and other open space should be allowed for, and should be left unplanted (see below).

Variation will also occur naturally as the woodland develops:

- Other species will move in by natural colonisation. Unplanted species, already on the site, may increase in number. Management may be needed of undesirable species.

- Some of the young trees may die, or fail to thrive. Typically 10% is allowable, for example under grant schemes, but if more than this fail, the site may fail to develop as woodland.

- Some species will grow at the expense of others. This may have been allowed for in the plan, or may be unexpected! Some species may fail due to disease or damage by animals. Squirrels for example tend to target particular species at a certain stage in their development (p107).

'Intimate' mixtures, where trees are planted singly in a random pattern across the site, are not recommended. Slower growing trees may be suppressed by fast growing trees, and thinning is difficult to carry out. Visually the result is rather homogenous, so the woodland lacks character. Although an intimate mixture may appear to be more natural, and have more wildlife diversity than a group mixture (as shown above), this is unlikely to be the case, because establishment of the woodland will be more difficult.

Single species woodlands can be created by planting the entire site with one species, and then thinning successively. Alternatively, the final crop species can be planted in small groups, say three or five trees at 3m spacing, with the spaces between the groups planted with nurse or understorey species, which are removed as the woodland matures. The groups of final crop species are progressively thinned to leave one tree. Single species woodlands are not natural, but they can be very attractive, and have a special character which can make them locally important features. They are suitable for small areas of woodland because they are easy to establish, and may have more visual impact than a mixed patch of woodland.

Coppice

A new coppice is fairly straightforward to plan and establish, as the plants which are to form the stools are planted at their final spacing. Areas of coppice (called coupes) are normally of one species, so that they grow up at the same rate and can be cut at the same time. Mixed species coppice can also be grown.

Table 2a: Short rotation coppice

SPECIES	MAIN USE	ROTATION	SPACING	NO/HECTARE
Willow	Baskets, willow sculptures	2-3 years	c. 2m	2250
Sweet chestnut	Walking sticks	3 years	c. 2m	2250
Hazel	Hurdles, bean poles, thatching spars	7-10 years	c. 2.5m	1500-2000

Table 2b: Long rotation coppice

SPECIES	MAIN USE	ROTATION	SPACING	NO/HECTARE
Alder	Turnery	10-20 years	c. 3m	1100
Sycamore	Turnery	10-20 years	c. 3m	1100
Ash	Turnery, tool handles, rails	10-25 years	c. 3m	1100
Sweet chestnut	Fencing	15-20 years	c. 3.5m	800-1000
Birch	Turnery	15-25 years	c. 3.5m	800-1000
Hornbeam	Firewood	15-35 years	c. 3.5m	800-1000
Lime	Turnery	20-25 years	c. 3.5m	800-1000
Oak	Fencing	18-35	c. 4.5m	200-500

Coppicing can be categorised as follows:

- Short rotation coppice, worked on rotations of less than 10 years, for pea and bean sticks, baskets, hurdles, firewood and other uses, including biomass for energy generation. Typical species are willow (osier), hazel and sweet chestnut.

- Long rotation coppice, worked on rotations of between 10 and 30+ years, for turnery, fencing, tool handles, firewood, charcoal and other uses. All broadleaved species can be grown this way, but species commonly used are alder, ash, birch, hornbeam, lime, oak and sycamore.

The table on the previous page gives examples of different uses, rotations and spacing.

Coppice with standards

Standards, usually of oak, are grown at between 30-100 per hectare (16-10m spacing), depending on age and size. For a new woodland, they should be planted at the same time as the coppice species are planted, at about 100 per hectare. At each coppice rotation, some of the standards can be felled, with replacement planting or protection of natural regeneration as required, to ensure continuity of cover.

Wood pasture and parkland

Wood pasture type cover may have evolved naturally in response to grazing pressures from herds of wild animals. Regeneration would have occurred naturally in response to seed years and periods of declining grazing pressure. During the middle ages, trees in wood pastures and wooded commons were important resources for fuel, fodder and other uses, and effort must have been put into ensuring that regeneration succeeded. Numbers of trees per acre were not specified, as they were for coppice with standards for example, although pollarded trees were often identified

in documents, which indicates their importance.

Many of the landscape parks of the 17th and 18th centuries were created by moving quite large trees (p3). In modern times, most of this type of planting has been of standard trees, protected as necessary with individual tree surrounds. Establishment may be improved by planting closely-spaced groups of trees and shrubs, and then thinning, as described above. Fairly early thinning is required, to ensure that the final trees develop the wide branching habit and well developed rooting system of trees grown in open ground.

Today, management of wood pastures and wooded commons is aimed at conserving veteran trees, and managing grazing to permit natural regeneration as necessary. Management of invasive species, particularly bracken, is often needed.

A modern form of wood pasture is agroforestry, which is the growing of trees on land also used for agriculture, which may be under grass for grazing or fodder, or cultivated for crops. Agroforestry is eligible for grant aid under the Woodland Grant Scheme (p116).

Spinneys and woodland edges

Spinneys, scrub and woodland edges should be closely planted as shown in the diagram below. Weeding will be necessary for 2-3 years, depending on the situation and soil type, but the thicket of growth should rapidly close and shade out grasses and other competing species. Brambles that occur naturally may be a useful addition, provided they are not so abundant as to smother the planted species. Self-thinning will occur, as individual plants become suppressed by others, and thinning operations are not normally necessary. To increase diversity in large areas of scrub, parts can be cut on rotation. Many of these species can spread quite rapidly, and management by mowing or grazing may be needed to maintain grassy open areas within patches of scrub.

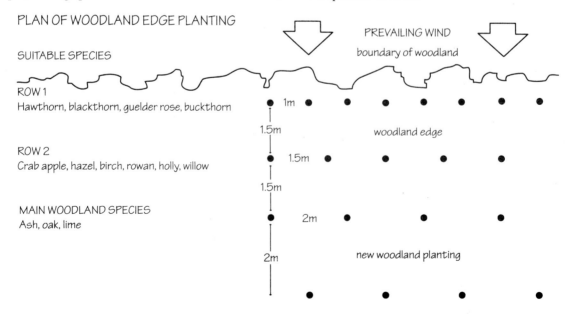

PLAN OF WOODLAND EDGE PLANTING

SUITABLE SPECIES

ROW 1
Hawthorn, blackthorn, guelder rose, buckthorn

ROW 2
Crab apple, hazel, birch, rowan, holly, willow

MAIN WOODLAND SPECIES
Ash, oak, lime

PREVAILING WIND
boundary of woodland

1m
1.5m
woodland edge

1.5m
1.5m

2m
new woodland planting

2m

Map of local seed zones

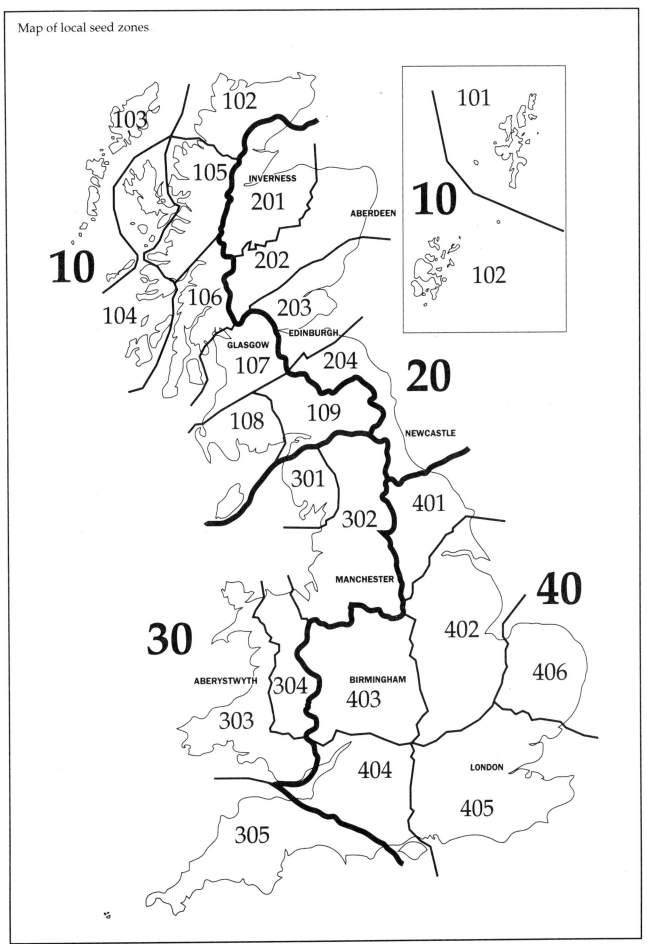

(Map and tables on pages 18 and 19 reproduced with permission from *Using Local Stock for Planting Native Trees and Shrubs,* Forestry Commission, 1999)

Table 2c   Native species appropriate to the numbered zones

Large and medium sized trees		Seed zone number (see map)																									Soils					
Species		101	102	103	104	105	106	107	108	109	201	202	203	204	301	302	303	304	305	401	402	403	404	405	406	a	b	c	d	e	f
alder, black	Alnus glutinosa	●	●	●	●	●	●	●	●	●	●	●	●	●	●	●	●	●	●	●	●	●	●	●	●	●				●	
apple, crab	Malus sylvestris ssp sylvestris			●	●	●	●	●	●	●	●	●	●	●	●	●	●	●	●	●	●	●	●	●	●					●	
ash	Fraxinus excelsior	●	●	●	●	●	●	●	●	●	●	●	●	●	●	●	●	●	●	●	●	●	●	●	●	●	●	●		●	●
aspen	Populus tremula	●	●	●	●	●	●	●	●	●	●	●	●	●	●	●	●	●	●	●	●	●	●	●	●	●	●	●		●	●
beech	Fagus sylvatica																													●	●
birch, downy	Betula pubescens	●	●	●	●	●	●	●	●	●	●	●	●	●	●	●	●	●	●	●	●	●	●	●	●	●	●	●		●	●
birch, silver	Betula pendula	●	●	●	●	●	●	●	●	●	●	●	●	●	●	●	●	●	●	●	●	●	●	●	●		●	●		●	●
cherry, bird	Prunus padus	●		●	●	●	●	●	●	●	●	●	●	●	●	●	●	●	●	●	●	●	●	●	●	●				●	
cherry, gean	Prunus avium		●	●	●	●	●	●	●	●	●	●	●	●	●	●	●	●	●	●	●	●	●	●	●		●	●		●	●
elm, wych	Ulmus glabra	●	●	●	●	●	●	●	●	●	●	●	●	●	●	●	●	●	●	●	●	●	●	●	●			●		●	
hornbeam	Carpinus betulus																													●	
lime, sm leaved	Tilia cordata								●				●												●	●				●	
lime, lge leaved	Tilia platyphyllos									●																	●			●	
maple, field	Acer campestre									●			●												●					●	
oak, common	Quercus robur	●	●	●	●	●	●	●	●	●	●	●	●	●	●	●	●	●	●	●	●	●	●	●	●	●	●	●		●	●
oak, sessile	Quercus petraea	●	●	●	●	●	●	●	●	●	●	●	●	●	●	●	●	●	●	●	●	●	●	●	●			●		●	●
pine, Scots	Pinus sylvestris	●								●					●												●			●	●
poplar, black	Populus nigra var. betulifolia																													●	
poplar, grey	Populus canescens																													●	
rowan	Sorbus aucuparia	●	●	●	●	●	●	●	●	●	●	●	●	●	●	●	●	●	●	●	●	●	●	●	●	●	●			●	●
service tree	Sorbus torminalis																													●	
whitebeam	Sorbus aria sensu lato		●												●												●			●	●
willow, crack	Salix fragilis		●	●			●	●	●	●	●	●	●	●	●	●	●	●	●	●	●	●	●	●	●	●		●		●	●
willow, goat	Salix caprea	●	●	●	●	●	●	●	●	●	●	●	●	●	●	●	●	●	●	●	●	●	●	●	●	●		●		●	●
willow, white	Salix alba		●	●	●		●	●																	●	●				●	●
yew	Taxus baccata																							●			●			●	

Soils: a = wet sites   b = light, dry soils   c = heavy soils   d = acid   e = neutral or alkaline   f = exposed sites   For information on species native to Northern Ireland, see Our Trees (BTCV, 1996).

Table 2c Native species appropriate to the numbered zones (continued)

Small trees and shrubs		Seed zone number (see map)																								Soils					
Species		101	102	103	104	105	106	107	108	109	201	202	203	204	301	302	303	304	305	401	402	403	404	405	406	a	b	c	d	e	f
blackthorn	*Prunus spinosa*	●	●	●	●	●	●	●	●	●	●	●	●	●	●	●	●	●	●	●	●	●	●	●	●	●	●	●		●	●
box	*Buxus sempervirens*																		●				●	●			●		●	●	
broom	*Cytisus scoparius*	●	●	●	●	●	●	●	●	●	●				●	●	●	●	●	●	●	●	●	●	●	●	●		●		●
buckthorn, ald.	*Frangula alnus*									●			●		●	●	●	●	●	●	●	●	●	●	●					●	
buckthorn, prg.	*Rhamnus catharticus*									●			●		●	●	●	●	●	●	●	●	●	●	●			●	●	●	
butchers broom	*Ruscus aculeatus*																								●				●	●	
dogwood	*Cornus sanguinea*								●	●	●				●	●	●	●	●	●	●	●	●	●	●		●	●		●	
elder	*Sambucus nigra*	●	●	●	●	●	●	●	●	●	●				●	●	●	●	●	●	●	●	●	●	●		●	●	●	●	
gorse	*Ulex europaeus*	●	●	●	●	●	●	●	●	●	●	●	●	●	●	●	●	●	●	●	●	●	●	●	●	●	●	●	●		●
guelder rose	*Viburnum opulus*	●	●	●	●	●	●	●	●	●	●			●	●	●	●	●	●	●	●	●	●	●	●		●	●		●	
hawthorn, com.	*Crataegus monogyna*	●	●	●	●	●	●	●	●	●	●	●	●	●	●	●	●	●	●	●	●	●	●	●	●		●	●	●	●	●
hawthorn, Mid.	*Crataegus laevigata*	●	●	●	●	●	●	●	●	●	●			●	●	●	●	●	●	●	●	●	●	●	●		●	●		●	
hazel	*Corylus avellana*	●	●	●	●	●	●	●	●	●	●			●	●	●	●	●	●	●	●	●	●	●	●		●			●	●
holly	*Ilex aquifolium*	●	●	●	●	●	●	●	●	●	●	●			●	●	●	●	●	●	●	●	●	●	●		●			●	
juniper	*Juniperus communis*	●	●	●					●	●	●				●	●	●	●	●	●	●	●	●	●	●		●	●	●	●	●
privet	*Ligustrum vulgare*	●	●						●	●	●				●	●	●	●	●	●	●	●	●	●	●		●	●		●	●
rose, dog	*Rosa canina*	●	●	●	●	●	●	●	●	●	●	●			●	●	●	●	●	●	●	●	●	●	●		●	●		●	●
rose, field	*Rosa arvensis*											●			●	●	●	●	●	●	●	●	●	●	●			●		●	
spindle	*Euonymus europaeus*											●			●	●	●	●	●	●	●	●	●	●	●			●		●	
spurge laurel	*Daphne laureola*									●					●	●	●	●	●	●	●	●	●	●	●			●		●	
wayfaring tree	*Viburnum lantata*														●	●	●	●	●	●	●	●	●					●		●	
willow, almond	*Salix triandra*										●			●	●	●	●	●	●	●	●	●	●	●	●	●				●	
willow, bay	*Salix pentandra*								●	●	●	●			●	●	●	●	●	●	●	●	●	●	●	●		●		●	
willow, eared	*Salix aurita*	●	●	●	●	●	●	●	●	●	●	●			●	●	●	●	●	●	●	●	●	●	●	●		●		●	
willow, grey	*Salix cinerea*	●	●	●	●	●	●	●	●	●	●	●			●	●	●	●	●	●	●	●	●	●	●	●		●	●	●	●
willow, osier	*Salix viminalis*	●	●	●	●	●	●	●	●	●	●	●			●	●	●	●	●	●	●	●	●	●	●	●		●	●	●	●
willow, purple	*Salix purpurea*		●	●	●	●	●	●	●	●	●	●			●	●	●	●	●	●	●	●	●	●	●	●		●		●	●

Soils: a = wet sites b = light, dry soils c = heavy soils d = acid e = neutral or alkaline f = exposed sites

For information on species native to Northern Ireland, see *Our Trees* (BTCV, 1996).

Species

NATIVE SPECIES

Species which are native to the local area should be the first choice when planting woodlands for wildlife and amenity. Planting such species helps maintain distinctive local types of woodland, and helps form the basis of woodland ecosystems which are adapted to local conditions. Stock of local provenance (see below) can be bought from tree nurseries, or you can propagate your own stock from locally collected seed (chapter 5).

The map and tables below are reproduced with permission from the publication *Using Local Stock for Planting Native Trees and Shrubs* (Forestry Commission, 1999), which should be consulted for full details.

The Forestry Commission is promoting the use of plants of local provenance for planting in semi-natural woodlands, or where native woodlands are to be created by planting. The voluntary system described in the leaflet has been introduced to provide a framework for supplying trees of local provenance. The system is of great importance to the British tree nursery industry, as there is a strong interest in planting local species, but until the introduction of this system, there was no standard for deciding what constituted 'local', or of knowing from where the seed of purchased trees had been gathered. The system has relevance for seed gatherers, growers of trees, landscape designers, and those who buy and plant trees.

It includes:

- Guidance to seed collectors on methods of identifying individual trees which are likely to be of local origin (see map p17).

- A system for issuing a Certificate of Local Provenance to identify the source of particular seeds and seedlings.

- Information which gives planters and designers clear information on which species are appropriate for the area where they wish to plant.

Alterations may be made to various procedures as the system is adopted, but within a few years it should mean that plants of local provenance can be reliably obtained for all areas of the country.

The local seed zones have been drawn up based on climatic and geological variation. In the south east, where climatic differences are small, divisions have also taken account of broad patterns of the natural distribution of native species. Within each seed zone conditions are broadly similar, and therefore seed collected from trees long growing in that zone, is thought to be the best match to provide stock for planting in that zone.

From the list of species appropriate to your local seed zone, trees and shrubs must also be chosen according to their suitability to different soil types and degrees of exposure.

NON-NATIVE SPECIES

Woodlands planted for timber production may include non-native or non-local species where these are planted to produce a commercial crop for a particular market. However, it should be noted that historically many such plantations have not repaid their investment because markets have changed by the time the crop matures.

Non-native or non-local species may have a role on very exposed sites, where they act as a nurse to the desired final species. Likewise, some soils which are highly disturbed, very low in nutrients or contaminated may only be able to support woodland cover of non-native species.

Of the introduced species, only conifers have been widely used in plantations, with sweet chestnut planted for coppicing. Particular strains of poplar and willow have been planted for commercial use. Most other introduced species have been planted in parks and gardens, and have not been generally used to create areas of woodland.

Of the native species with limited range, beech and Scot's pine have been widely planted throughout Britain. Introduced or selected strains of oaks and other trees have been planted in existing woodlands and in plantations, with the aim of producing higher quality commercial timber.

There are many publications on various aspects of non-native trees, ranging from their use in parks and gardens, to the silviculture of non-native trees in plantations. The Forestry Commission publish detailed information on species with commercial value, and other selected titles are given in the bibliography. Some tree nursery catalogues give useful information on the use of non-native species which they supply.

Woodland layout

Woodland edges, both on the outside of the wood, and along tracks and glades within the woodland area, are very valuable habitats. They provide a range of conditions of light and shade, shelter and exposure, and can support a wide variety of plants from mosses and lichens, herbs and grasses through to shrubs and trees. The management of the edge is very important in providing sheltered conditions for the woodland within. The woodland edges are also the parts which are most valued by people for recreation, although woodland edges which are 'overgrown' may also invoke feelings of fear. Rides, glades and clearings not only provide open, sheltered, sunny spaces within the wood, but add to the amount of woodland edge.

Table 2d Site requirements and characteristics of native tree species

Species	wet ground	light sandy soil	heavy soil	acid	alkaline	OK in shade	average ultimate height			growth rate			tolerant of sites that are:			valuable for:	
							0.5m to 5m	6m to 15m	16m+	fast	med	slow	polluted	coastal	exposed	birds	insects
alder	★				●	●		●		●					●		●
ash	●	●	●		●	●			●		●		●	●	●		
aspen			●	●	●				●	●			●	●	●		●
beech		●			●	●			●		●						●
birch, downy	●			●					●	●			●		●		●
birch, silver		●		●					●	●			●		●		●
cherry, wild		●						●			●		●				
crab apple		●	●	●	●			●				●	●			●	●
elm, wych			●		●	●			●		●		●			●	●
hawthorn		●	●	●	●	●	●					●	●	●	●	●	●
hawthorn, midland			●		●	●	●					●		●	●	●	●
hazel		●	●	●	●	●		●		●					●		●
holly			●	●	●	●		●				●		●	●	●	
hornbeam	■		●		●				●		●						
juniper		●		●	●			●							●		
lime, small leaved			●		●	●			●		●		●		●		●
lime, large leaved			●		●				●		●		●				●
maple, field				●	●	●		●			●		●				
oak, pedunculate	■		●		●				●		●				●	●	●
oak, sessile	●	●		●	●	●			●		●				●	●	●
pine, Scots		●		●					●		●				●		●
poplar, black	▲	●	●		●				●	●							●
rowan		●	●	●	●			●		●			●	●	●	●	
whitebeam, common		●	●		●			●			●						●
wild service			●		●	●		●			●					●	
willow, crack	★				●			●		●			●	●	●	●	●
willow, white	★				●			●		●			●	●	●	●	●
yew		●			●	●		●				●	●		●	●	

★ Only species to survive on sites that are with anaerobic soil conditions

■ Will do well on sites that are seasonally wet

▲ Will only tolerate wet ground if there is some seasonality or 'flushing' (water movement) within the soil and subsoil

Most woodlands have a proportion of open space, and plantations and other woods require roads and tracks for management. The Woodland Grant Scheme (p116) normally permits 20% open space of the total area receiving grant, with trees planted at 2250 per hectare (2m spacing) or 1100 per hectare (3m spacing). For woods not receiving grant aid, up to 30% open space may be appropriate. More than about 50% open space creates a park or pasture wood landscape, with clumps or bands of trees with linked open spaces. The nature of open space will change as the trees grow (see diagrams below).

ACCESS

First mark any existing access routes across the site, either official rights of way or other unofficial paths. These paths are likely already to follow the shortest and easiest route, and there is no point in making them longer or more difficult. The use of 'desire lines' is strong, and young trees will not survive the trampling of existing patterns of use. In large areas of planting, it's possible to leave sufficient space between the trees that the path or ride remains open to the sunlight. This needs a strip at least 12m wide. In smaller areas of planting there is not space for such wide rides at the same time as creating a mainly woodland habitat, and paths will need to go under the canopy.

Minor paths which are to go under the canopy can be planned at this stage, or can be left to be created by use or clearance as the woodland develops. Generally it's easier

to plan paths at the beginning of the project, when the best routes can be picked out on the ground, and before they are obscured by growth.

Avoid creating wind-tunnels, which will lessen the value of tracks and rides for wildlife or recreation. Rides can be angled just before emerging from the woodland, especially at edges which face the prevailing wind. Occasional distinct curves along rides will lessen the wind tunnel effect, and bays and scallops along the woodland edge (see below) will help provide sheltered conditions.

The width, orientation and height of the surrounding trees affects the conditions of sun and shade. East/west orientations give more sun during the summer, whereas a north/south orientation gives more sun in the winter. Generally, open rides need to be 1.5 times as wide as the height of the surrounding trees. A ride running through mature woodland of lime, ash, beech, oak or hornbeam, which may reach 20-30m height, will need to be at least 30-45m wide to benefit those species, and especially butterflies, which need the most sunlight. This width of ride is only possible in large woodlands of 10 hectares or more.

In a coppiced wood, where the maximum tree height is reduced by frequent cutting, rides can be narrower and remain sunny. A hazel coppice, for example, might reach a height of about 6m before it is cut, so rides of about 9m width will remain open to the sun. Typical species of a spinney are the small, spiny species of hawthorn and blackthorn, through which it is also easier to retain sunny

RIDES AND PATHS IN WOODLAND
Sample area: one hectare (100x100m)

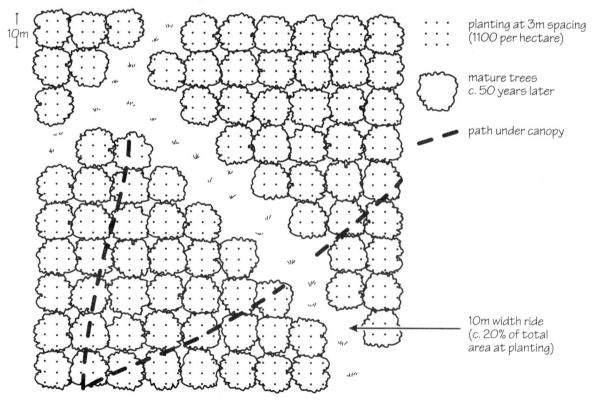

10m

· · ·
· · · planting at 3m spacing
· · · (1100 per hectare)

mature trees
c. 50 years later

– – – path under canopy

10m width ride
(c. 20% of total
area at planting)

open space. Copses and spinneys are good ways of providing woody cover on small patches of land, but will not develop the diversity of a woodland.

OPEN SPACES

If the area is greater than about one hectare, it will be feasible to make one or more open glades within the woodland. These should normally be linked with paths to ease management. A glade needs to be at least 500 square metres in order to retain its open character as the trees around it grow up. In mature woodland, where trees are 20-30m tall, an open space needs to be at least 2,500 square metres, or a quarter of a hectare, to retain its open, sunny character.

Ground treatment

If starting with bare ground, rides and other spaces can be sown with suitable mixtures of native seeds, or can be left to regenerate naturally (p103). Where rides and open spaces are already grassy, the easiest option is to retain the grass cover, and mow it as necessary. Collect up the mowings and pile them up nearby to be used later as mulch around the trees. Collection will help impoverish the grass, so that other species are able to move in. Removal of turf to create patches of bare ground may be an option. Gravel surfacing laid down for tracks or paths is not necessarily a minus for biodiversity, but may develop a more varied flora than was there previously.

EDGES

Within the boundaries of the planting site, define the edges. These should be varied to fit the landform, drainage patterns, and to take account of views into and out of the site. Where the site abuts onto private gardens it is essential to consult residents, who will not want their gardens or houses shaded or their views obscured. In an area surrounded by housing, a central clump of planting, with smaller clumps grading to the edges of the site may be more acceptable than a solid block of woodland. An area of mown grass around the woodland will enhance its appearance, and increase accessibility into the woodland.

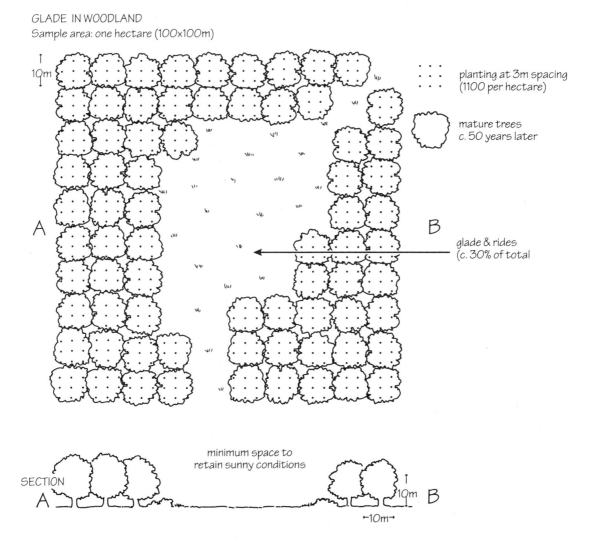

GLADE IN WOODLAND
Sample area: one hectare (100x100m)

10m

planting at 3m spacing
(1100 per hectare)

mature trees
c. 50 years later

A

B

glade & rides
(c. 30% of total

minimum space to
retain sunny conditions

SECTION

A

B

10m

←10m→

Management of edges

The management of edges, both those on the outside and those within the wooded area, needs to be planned at an early stage, as it will affect the choice of species and spacing. The planning of edge planting is also very important for shelter, with those on the outer, windward edge of the wood being most important (p16). The most valuable edges for insects and birds are the sunny south and west facing edges, so it's best to concentrate effort on edges with these aspects.

For diversity of wildlife along the edges of glades and rides, a three-zone system is best. As shown in the diagram, the shrub layer is coppiced, and the tall herbaceous layer and the grassy verge are mown, at the varied frequencies shown. Note though that this system may not be compatible with encouraging feelings of safety (p25).

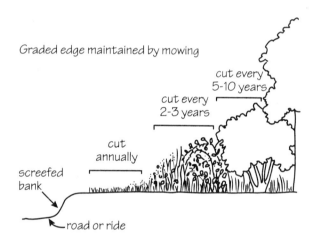

Graded edge maintained by mowing

cut every 5-10 years

cut every 2-3 years

cut annually

screefed bank

road or ride

Diversity can be increased more if alternate edges are cut in different years, as shown below.

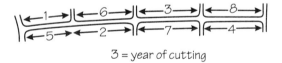

3 = year of cutting

Bays or scallops can be incorporated into the design of a road or ride to provide a natural, undulating line. If placed in opposing positions, more light across the ride will be created. The smallest bay length which is useful is 7m (23'), but if the trees have an ultimate height of more than 20m (66'), bays will need to be a minimum of 25m (83') long to admit enough light.

At intersections of rides and tracks, larger glades which allow light in from various angles can be created by leaving the corners unplanted.

Trying to create glades or widen rides in existing woodland is not easy. This will open up the woodland, typically leaving an exposed edge of bare trunks and branches which looks unattractive, and exposes the woodland to cold winds and possible wind damage.

PONDS AND STREAMS

Ponds, streams and marshy ground are valuable habitats in themselves, and their presence in a woodland greatly increases the site's diversity, as well as adding to its amenity value. However, heavily shaded ponds are of much less

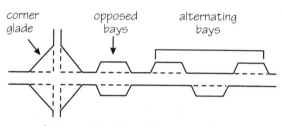

corner glade

opposed bays

alternating bays

Glades and scalloped bays on road- or rideside

wildlife value, and it's important that new planting does not encroach on their open, sunny margins. With streams, at least half should be open to sunlight, with the remaining portion under intermittent shade from light-canopy trees and shrubs.

Herbicides should not be used within 10m (33') of streams, or 20m (66') of reservoirs.

LOCAL IDENTITY

At an early stage, name the wood and give a name to the features within it. Choose names with local associations, or which relate to the physical features of the site or the activities various areas are used for. Such names usually arise naturally amongst people who use the site, but it's easier if there is a consensus about what is what! Obvious and sensible names refer to the species planted, for example, 'the birches' or 'the alders', or to the planting pattern or structure of the trees, for example 'the avenue' or 'the coppice'. Valleys, ridges and ponds are obvious features for naming, along with use-related locations such as 'the picnic place', 'the cricket pitch'. Sometimes the shape of a space or area of planting leads to a name such 'the airstrip' or 'the triangle'. If the new woodland incorporates some existing trees, you may find that any old or unusual trees have local names. Trees used for climbing and play quickly acquire names among local children.

Fear of woodlands

Many people have a fear of woods. These feelings include:

- Fear of being attacked. This fear is strongest among women, and is the main reason why many women would not consider going alone into a wooded area. It also affects the freedom allowed to children to play in and around woodlands.

- Fear of woodlands providing cover for unsocial or criminal behaviour. Residents may not welcome plans to plant woodlands in the vicinity of their homes, because of the fear of it attracting unsavoury or criminal behaviour.

- Fear of getting lost. This is not just a fear of not being able to find the way out of the wood, but also that help would not be accessible in the case of an accident or injury.

The intrinsic quality of a wood is such that it is impossible to design away the features that make it frightening to some people. These include undergrowth, limited sightlines and low levels of light. The only way to make woods feel safe to people who fear them is to make sure there are plenty of other people around. People do not fear a crowd, or not often a group, but they do fear meeting a 'loner'.

Some people's enjoyment of a wood is spoiled by the presence of too many other people, and wildlife suffers if there is frequent disturbance. Large woods can be zoned into quiet and busy areas, by the way access is laid out, by the provision of picnic areas, play equipment and so on, and by management of the understorey. In some cases the wood may provide the setting in which activities take place, such as playtrails, cycling or fishing. On the larger scale, most people want to live and work in attractive wooded landscapes, but not to feel enclosed by trees. The Community Forests (p4) are aiming for 30% woodland cover.

PEOPLING A WOOD

- If possible, site new woodland planting where there is already a well-established access route, such as a footpath, cycle-track, well-used short cut or other route, which will automatically bring people into the wooded area. Consultation will be needed, together with the application of some of the design guidelines below, so that existing patterns of use are not discouraged.

- Work in the wood as much as possible, for example coppicing, planting, footpath work or mowing glades.

- Organise guided walks, woodland days, children's activities, treasure hunts, orienteering, birdwatching and other events. For children, the sort of activities that used to happen informally can be the easiest and most successful, such as building dens, damming streams, having bonfires or laying trails.

- Encourage responsible dog walkers, by providing parking, signs, dog toilet areas or dog bins. Regular dog walkers are amongst the highest users of open spaces near residential areas, and in the main, help reassure other users.

- Encourage joggers, by providing circular routes with good surfacing.

- Provide free parking.

DESIGN GUIDELINES

- Car parks should have a straightforward layout, rather than a design with bays hidden by shrubs, where theft or mugging can occur unseen. Clear undergrowth from the edges, and preferably make car parks easily visible from the road.

- Make access inviting at the edges, so there are lots of easy routes into the wood from around its edges. Generally make the edges open, with glades, well-spaced trees and a lack of undergrowth, although this will lessen the value of the edges for wildlife, and decrease their shelter value.

- Provide clear, wide, well-surfaced main paths through the woodland. Use will then be concentrated along these routes, which will help create feelings of safety in numbers. Other paths can be provided for the more adventurous.

- Provide long sightlines along the main paths, by making long, generally straight or gently curving sections. Make junctions wide and open.

- Provide wide grassy margins to the paths, with no undergrowth. Remove the understorey from the adjacent edges of the wood.

- Site open areas for picnics and play near to car-parks, access points, visitor centres and buildings, so users feel there is help or supervision nearby.

- Provide clear signs, giving distances to destinations or exit points from the wood. These should be multi-lingual as appropriate to the area.

- Do not purposely block views of buildings and roads with planting, as woodland users may prefer to stay within sight of other people. Tall buildings, pylons and chimneys can act as useful reference points against getting lost. Designers may prefer to create the illusion of wilderness and isolation, but visitors may prefer the opposite.

- Provide maps of the wood which show access routes, distances, picnic areas and different zones as appropriate. It is important to show the wood in relation to the surrounding area, and not in isolation. As in the point above, feelings of safety will be encouraged if people know the various exit routes from the wood, and any links to roads, housing, shops and other familiar places.

- Remove all signs of social disorder, such as graffiti, rubbish or abandoned cars.

- Upgrade the general appearance of the wood. This includes keeping fences, paths, seats and other built features in good order. It may also mean removal of scrub, mowing of grass and other actions which may have some adverse effects for wildlife, but which will help attract more people into the wood.

For further details, see *Growing in Confidence – understanding people's perceptions of urban fringe woodlands* (Countryside Commission 1995).

Non-woodland planting

This includes avenues, orchards, arboreta or individual trees in parks, gardens and streets. Arboreta and orchards by their nature comprise non-native species, and non-natives may also be the appropriate choice for many ornamental plantings. Although these trees can be valuable for wildlife, they will not develop the range of organisms associated with native trees, but features other than their ecological value may have priority. Many street trees, avenues or groupings of ornamental trees may be far more important to the local community than trees or woodland which are ecologically more valuable.

Values include:

- Landscape and local identity.

- Screening and shelter. Trees may screen unattractive views, give privacy, shelter and shade.

- Environmental value, in reducing run-off, absorbing carbon dioxide, counteracting the 'heat island' effect of cities.

- Improving the appearance of and value placed on local areas.

- Botanical interest.

- Amenity and recreation. A wood-pasture, park, golf course or similar landscape of grass and trees is an 'ideal landscape' for many people.

The advice to plant small trees, and to keep them weed-free for at least three years remains the same, whether you are planting an individual tree or many hundreds. However, it may be more difficult to obtain non-native species, or particular cultivars of native species, as transplants, and they are more often sold as whips or standard trees. Fruit trees are normally grafted onto particular root stocks which limit the growth of the tree, and are sold as bush, half-standard or standard trees (p68).

Species must be chosen with care, taking particular note of the space available and the recommended planting distances from buildings (p30). The larger native species such as oak, beech, ash and small-leaved lime can achieve a spread of 20-30m (60-100') when grown in open ground, and are only suitable for planting in very spacious surroundings. Smaller native or introduced trees may be more suitable than large native species for non-woodland planting, because they require less space.

Apart from street trees, nearly all these types of plantings are intended to result in well-spaced, clear-stemmed trees surrounded with grass. However, for successful establishment it is essential that the trees are not grown in a grass surround until they are about ten years old. Grass, and particularly mown grass, competes strongly with young trees (p97), and mowers can damage or kill trees!

At the planning stage, you must take into account the management of the area between the trees in the decade or so after planting. There are various approaches given below. Whichever method you choose, the cost in time and money of the purchase and planting of the final trees is likely to be a small proportion of the amount invested in creating the conditions in which the young trees will flourish. However, the familiar sight of groups of long-planted but struggling trees in a grass surround is the reason this investment must be made.

SMALL GROUPS OF TREES

One of the three following methods can be used:

- Plant the final trees amongst a matrix of shrubs or trees at a spacing of 2 or 3m, as for woodland planting (p14). The final trees can be planted singly, or in groups of three or five, from which further selection takes place during thinning. In the first few years the thicket of growth will provide mutual shelter, and protect the final trees from damage by vandals or mowers. The shrubs and trees nearest to the final trees can be coppiced or removed after about five years to give the final trees space to spread. If the final trees grow up with too much competition, they will not produce sufficient side branches to make a balanced shape, nor sufficiently spreading roots to be stable when the other trees and shrubs are removed. Keep all the trees and shrubs weed-free by herbicides or mulches (chapter 6), preferably keeping the whole area weed-free. If planting is at 2m spacings, the required 1m diameter weed-free area around each tree will anyway result in the whole area being weed-free. The thicket stage is valuable for wildlife, but blocks views and may not be popular with local residents. You also need to take into account the work involved in removing the unwanted trees or shrubs (p111).

• Plant only the final trees, but keep more than the minimum 1m grass-free circle around each tree. A 2m grass-free circle using mulch, herbicide or surface cultivation will be repaid by significantly better tree growth. This method gives no protection to the trees from vandals, mowers or accidental damage, and the trees may need wire mesh protectors or similar. A large area of ground covered with plastic mulch or bare from herbicide application does not look attractive. A loose organic mulch, with or without residual herbicide or plastic mulch looks more acceptable, but is expensive.

• In school or hospital grounds, parks and large gardens, another approach is to surround the final trees with low-growing garden shrubs and ground cover plants. Even better is to plant into an existing shrub bed or border, where conditions will give trees a really good start. The young trees can unobtrusively establish amongst the shelter of the shrubs or other plants, safe from mowers and most vandals, and in soil which may already support beneficial mycorrhiza that do not occur under grass. Once the trees have grown to a significant size in their surroundings, the shrubs or other plants can be removed as required, and grass, bulbs or native woodland plants established amongst the trees. If making a new bed, choose cheap low growing shrubs such as spiraea or lonicera nitida, bought as bare-root hedging shrubs in winter. Berberis, dwarf gorse and other spiny shrubs are useful to deter access. Although

the cost of purchasing sufficient shrubs may seem expensive, in the long term it may be cheaper in labour costs to have a low-maintenance shrub border, rather than mown grass, and it will certainly benefit the trees. Perennials, annuals or even vegetables can be grown in the bed as desired, as long as the tree roots are not disturbed during cultivation.

ARBORETA, AVENUES AND INDIVIDUAL TREES

Collections of trees in arboreta, street trees and other trees planted singly may need protection from accidental or intentional damage. Introduced trees and cultivars of native trees are normally planted as feathered whips or standards, which will need staking until the roots have established. Individual trees should have a weed-free surround of at least 1m diameter, and preferably 2m, until they are well established. Wire mesh or timber guards may be needed against vandals or grazing animals or (p82).

Avenues are normally planted at their final spacing, and protected individually. However planting within a fenced strip in a matrix of shrubs or smaller trees as described above may be cost-effective.

See page 81 for details on planting standard trees.

HEDGES AND SHELTERBELTS

Hedges for enclosure of stock are typically of species which are thorny and dense and respond well to laying and clipping, with hawthorn the most popular species. Hedges are normally planted in a double row, with rows 37cm (15") apart, and plants 45cm (18") apart in the row. Keep the entire base of the hedge weed-free until the plants are established. Many other native species can be used for hedging, and can be managed either by clipping, laying or coppicing. For full details see *Hedging* (BTCV 1998).

Shelterbelts are narrow bands of trees planted to give shelter for crops, stock, gardens or settlements. They need to be carefully planned with denser planting of smaller species on the windward side, to create a smooth profile which directs the wind up over the taller species behind, with a minimum of turbulence caused beyond.

Shelterbelts have long been used in upland areas, and some are ancient features of the farming landscape. Any replacement planting should take into account their historic, landscape and wildlife value.

The design of shelterbelts must allow for wind permeability in order to avoid the formation of eddies. For optimum efficiency, about 40% permeability is needed. A shelterbelt can create shelter for about 20 times the height of the belt on the downwind side, and about three times the height on the

TREES IN SHRUB BED

PLAN

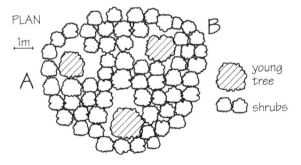

SECTION

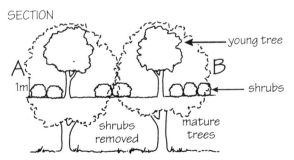

upwind side. The wind will sweep around the ends of the belt as well as over the top, leaving a triangular sheltered zone, as shown.

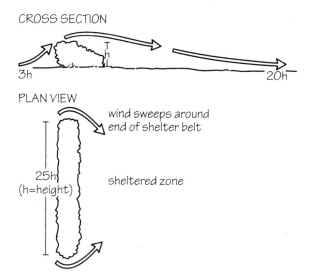

CROSS SECTION

PLAN VIEW

wind sweeps around end of shelter belt

25h (h=height)

sheltered zone

The base is the most important part of a shelterbelt, as if it becomes sparse, wind speeds are increased through the wood and into the area beyond. Remedying this situation is difficult because new plants cannot establish in such draughty conditions unless given artificial shelter.

Narrow belts, about 20m wide, are generally the most effective width for crop protection. Wider belts give no more shelter, and neither are they particularly suitable for timber production. The disadvantage of narrow belts is that they cannot be restored without clearing and replanting, and they are less attractive than wider strips as landscape and wildlife features.

The trees are usually planted using staggered or triangular spacing, so that they stand 2.4m (8') apart along rows that are 2.1m (7') apart. Each tree will then stand 2.4m (8') apart from adjacent trees (about 1916 trees per hectare). For most purposes an A-shaped profile is suitable, with the middle

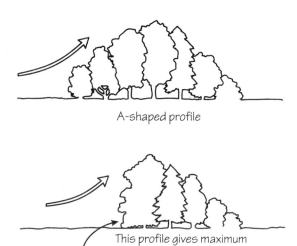

A-shaped profile

This profile gives maximum shelter for minimum width

ensure windward edge does not open up
- if necessary plant understorey shrubs

third planted with tall trees and the outer third planted with smaller trees and shrubs.

Avoid gaps, openings and re-entrants on the windward side of shelterbelts. If an opening is needed, make it oblique to the wind and plant the edges with wind-firm species.

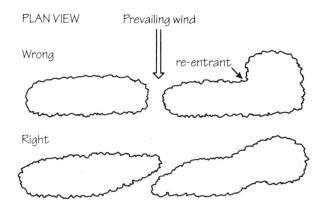

PLAN VIEW   Prevailing wind

Wrong

re-entrant

Right

Where the aim is maximum shelter for minimum width, plant tall, wind-firm species up to the windward edge, with smaller trees and shrubs along the leeward edge. Conifers should normally be interplanted with broadleaves to give winter shelter and act as a nurse crop.

Suitable species for shelterbelts

Given the appropriate soil and climate, suitable species include the following:

TALL   Lime, oak, sycamore, Scots pine

MEDIUM   Whitebeam, cherry, rowan

SMALL   Hawthorn, holly, hazel.

Establishment and maintenance

Three different approaches are outlined below:

- Nurse species can be planted, which will grow quickly and shelter the slower-growing, longer-lived species. Suitable conifers include Scots pine, and introduced species such as Sitka spruce, European larch and hybrid larch. In areas where rainfall reaches 75cm (30") annually, willow and poplar can also be used as a nurse. The nurse trees can either be planted in a strip along the windward edge with an outer strip of understorey shrubs, or can be mixed throughout the planting. Both methods have drawbacks. When a windward strip is felled or deteriorates, the increased exposure may damage the remaining trees. Nurse crops which are mixed throughout need careful thinning and removal to make sure the slower-growing species are not swamped.

- The belt can be established in two stages, planting half the width initially, and the other half as the planting begins to mature and becomes sparse at the base.

- Plant the full belt initially and thin it heavily at about 15 years, and more lightly thereafter at about 5 year intervals. At the same time underplant with shade-bearing shrubs, small trees, or successor species such as beech.

It's normally best to follow the example of similar successful shelterbelts in the locality. In coastal conditions for instance, plants which are generally tolerant of salt winds may not be so in every situation, and a tried and tested species is normally best. Some coastal localities are characterised by particular introduced species, such as holm oak, Monterey pine or tamarisk.

Old, sparse, ineffective shelterbelts can be revitalised in several ways. Where a belt casts a heavy shade, plant a new margin one to three rows deep along its windward edge. Then thin and underplant the old belt. Alternatively, replant existing gaps in the belt and then gradually extend the replanted areas by further fellings. A third method is to cut a series of V-shaped wedges through the width of the belt, starting at a point on the leeward edge. These should be replanted and progressively widened out by further fellings until the whole belt is gradually replanted.

Shelter for stock

In upland and exposed sites, woodland may be planted to provide shelter for stock.

Woods can be designed so that they offer shelter, whilst still being fenced. On open land where stock can move around the perimeter, blocks of woodland will give some shelter whichever way the wind is blowing. Some woods are planted in an L or X shape, to increase the length of edge. The permeability of the woodland is not significant, and any suitable species can be used.

Other woods for shelter can be partly or completely unfenced, allowing access for stock. This gives better shelter, but ground flora and tree roots can be damaged by trampling and browsing. Bark damage may occur, and natural re-generation may be prevented. A better method is to divide the woodland into three or four fenced compartments, using one per season in rotation. Additionally, natural regeneration can be protected by tree shelters.

TREES AND BUILDINGS

Problems associated with trees around buildings include those both above and below ground. Above ground problems include the following:

- Blocking of gutters with leaves or needles. Species with large leaves, such as sycamore and large-leaved lime, can cause blockage if they overhang gutters.

- Obstruction of light.

- Physical impact of branches on a building.

- Interference with overhead services.

Underground problems include the following:

- Drain blockage. Usually, tree roots will only penetrate a drain if it is already cracked. The roots then tend to grow towards the supply of water. A single root entering the crack can branch enough times to create a blockage.

- Physical damage by root growth. Generally, the major roots of a tree grow in a radial fashion from the stem base, within the top 30-50cm (12-20") of the soil. Although roots can laterally extend as much as 1.5 times the tree's height, most problems arising from the growth of roots will be located around the trunk of the tree. Common problems include paving being lifted or cracked, and walls being undermined.

- Damage from shrinkage of clay soils. Trees planted on shrinkable clay soils can dry the soil by removing water through their root systems. If any buildings are located nearby, subsidence of their foundations can occur. Deciduous broadleaved trees remove more water than evergreens and conifers. The table shows the minimum distances from buildings at which trees can be planted to avoid the danger of subsidence. Note that these are 'safe' minimum distances, as recommended by house insurers. Many existing urban trees are far nearer to buildings than this recommendation. However, with drought an increasing problem, it is suggested that these guidelines are followed for new planting in clay soils.

See overleaf for diagram showing minimum distances at which trees may be planted from housing to avoid subsidence.

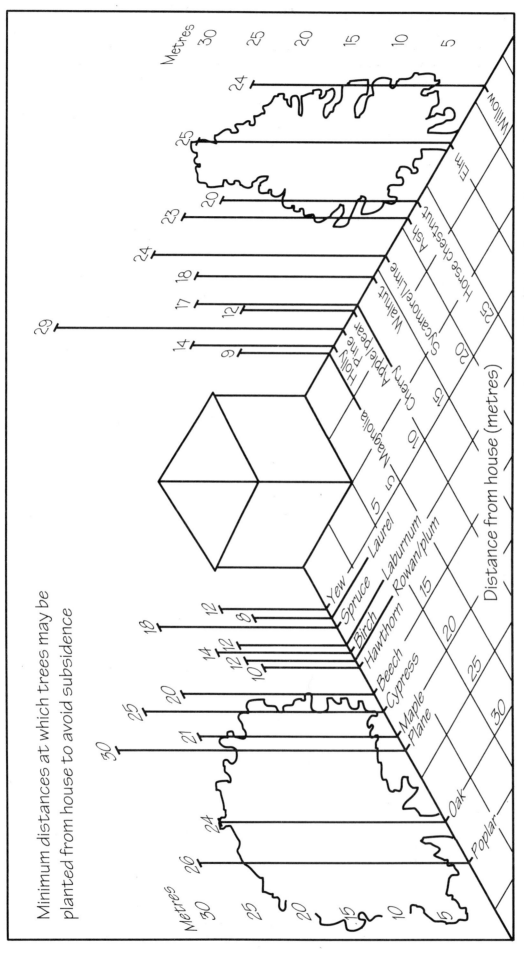

Minimum distances at which trees may be planted from house to avoid subsidence

Distance from house (metres)

Source: The Subsidence Claims Advisory Bureau

3   Trees and the law

A brief outline of some of the legal matters relating to trees:

The law relating to the use of land in the United Kingdom is complicated, and may differ across national boundaries. Rights and responsibilities between various government departments, non-governmental organisations and local authorities are not uniformly applied, and may change. Scotland has a different legal system to the rest of the UK.

- For advice relating to amenity trees or trees on public land, your best point of inquiry is normally through the tree officer at your local authority.

- For advice relating to trees on Sites of Special Scientific Interest, species or habitat protection, contact the nature conservation agency for England, Wales, Scotland or Northern Ireland (see below).

- For matters relating to commercial forestry, felling licences, control of deer or disease, contact the local office of the Forestry Commission for England, Wales and Scotland, or the Forest Service of the Department of Agriculture in Northern Ireland.

- For individual cases involving trees and private property, for example relating to boundaries, seek advice from a solicitor.

Tree preservation orders

Tree Preservation Orders (TPOs) are the principal means of planning control, in England and Wales, over the felling or maltreatment of amenity trees. TPOs can be made by a local authority to protect individual trees of exceptional amenity value, groups of trees and woodlands in the interests of good forestry or because of special amenity value, or all trees within a certain area, whether urban or rural. TPOs do not, however, normally include blanket protection over large areas. TPOs are designed to protect amenity trees which might be at risk, but not to hinder careful silvicultural management.

Tree Preservation Orders may:

- Prohibit the damage or destruction, felling, lopping, topping or uprooting of trees, except with the consent of the local authority.

- Ensure the replanting according to specified conditions of any part of woodland area which is felled as part of permitted forestry operations.

- Require the replacement as soon as reasonably possible of any tree (other than one which is part of a woodland) which is removed or destroyed in contravention of the order, or which dies. The replacement tree is protected by the original order.

Trees subject to a TPO should normally be visible from a road, footpath or other public place. Anyone can check whether TPOs are in force on any trees by contacting the local authority. There can be severe fines for contravention of TPOs.

Sites of special scientific interest

Sites of Special Scientific Interest (SSSIs) are designated by English Nature, the Countryside Council for Wales and Scottish Natural Heritage. In Northern Ireland, the Department of the Environment Northern Ireland has similar responsibilities for Areas of Special Scientific Interest (ASSIs). An owner whose land is designated a SSSI is sent a notification and a list of potentially damaging operations that should not be undertaken without prior consultation with the relevant agency. Under the terms of the Wildlife and Countryside Act 1981, payments may be made in some circumstances, for revenue forgone in SSSIs in the interests of nature conservation.

Conservation areas

These are areas in Britain of special architectural or historical interest, the character or appearance of which it is desirable to preserve or enhance. With certain exceptions, anyone proposing to cut down, top, lop or uproot a tree in a Conservation Area must give six weeks' notice of their intention to the local authority concerned. A felling licence (see below) may be required for the felling of trees. Trees may also be subject to a TPO, in which case the details given above apply.

Rights of way and public services

Some local and national authorities are empowered to fell trees for purposes of safety or access. Local authorities can cut back or fell trees and bushes which obscure public rights of way, including footpaths, or which obstruct light from street lamps or the sightlines of car drivers. Railway authorities, land drainage authorities, electricity authorities and BT can require removal of trees or parts of trees which may obstruct railways, rivers banks, power lines or telephone lines. Similar powers are available to providers of water, gas and oil, and airport authorities, to prevent risk of accident or damage to the installation, or to provide access to service routes.

The presence of overhead or underground services can influence woodland work, and any tree planting or other management in the vicinity of such services may require the permission of the appropriate authority.

Trees and boundaries

The intrusion of the roots or branches of a tree into adjacent properties can become a special form of legal nuisance. Relevant points include the following:

• If the roots or branches of a tree on one property penetrate or overhang a neighbour's land, this neighbour (who may be owner or tenant) is entitled to cut them off, as long as this is done on their side of the boundary. The boundary is presumed to run vertically up and down from the line at ground level. The neighbour cannot claim expenses from the tree-owner.

• Any cuttings remain the tree-owner's property, and cannot be utilised by the neighbour in any way. The neighbour can, however, place all cuttings on the owner's land. If the owner throws them back, the neighbour can claim for any financial loss incurred.

• If the neighbour must enter the owner's land to cut off overhanging branches, the neighbour must first serve notice of an intent to do so. The owner can then do the work personally if desired. Otherwise, the neighbour cannot be prevented from entering the land unless an injunction is obtained. A claim can however be made for any damages resulting from the neighbour's entry on the land.

• The neighbour must exercise every care to do no injury to overhanging trees when lopping off overhanging branches or penetrating roots.

Protection by general law

Trees, under the definition of private property, are protected by the law of tort. Anyone trespassing on an owner's land who injures a tree may have to pay damages to the owner as compensation. Factories which harm trees through the emission of toxic fumes may be prevented from further emission by a court injunction, and may also be liable for damages. Trees in a tended area (i.e. not growing wild) are protected from vandalism by the Criminal Damage Act

1971. Trees growing wild are also protected by this Act, except in respect to their foliage and fruit.

Unsafe trees

Unsafe trees under which the public has access, such as those overhanging highways, may constitute a public nuisance. If the tree appeared sound, but then fell or lost branches, the owner would not be liable for damages because the failure of the tree could not reasonably have been foreseen or prevented. If the tree had obvious signs of disease or weakness and then failed, however, the owner might be sued for any damage caused. It is therefore important to inspect such trees regularly to check on their condition.

Felling licences

A licence from the Forestry Commission is normally required to fell growing trees (though not for lopping and topping), but in any calendar quarter up to 5 cubic metres may be felled by an occupier or his/her agent, without a licence, provided that not more than 2 cubic metres are sold. A licence is not needed if any of the following conditions apply:

• The felling is in accordance with an approved plan of operations under one of the Forestry Commission grant schemes.

• The trees are in a garden, orchard, churchyard or public open space.

• The trees are all below 8cm (3") in diameter, measured 1.3m (4'3") from the ground; or in the case of thinnings, below 10cm (4") in diameter; or in the case of coppice or underwood, below 15cm (6") in diameter.

• The trees are interfering with permitted development or statutory work by public bodies.

• The trees are dead, dangerous, causing a nuisance or are badly affected by Dutch elm disease.

• The felling is done under an Act of Parliament.

4 Safety, equipment and organisation

The following information on safety and equipment is basic to most aspects of tree planting, tree nursery and aftercare operations. Tools suitable for coppicing and felling small trees are described, but felling of large trees is not covered by this handbook.

Safety precautions

GENERAL

- A suitable first aid kit (see below) must be on hand at the work site. There should be at least one Basic Trained First Aider on all BTCV practical projects, training courses or other events.

- All workers should be advised to be immunized against tetanus.

- Postpone the work if it is raining heavily. Once gloves, tools and the ground become sodden and slippery, there is an increased risk of injuring yourself or others.

- Wear suitable tough clothing (see below).

- Safety helmets should be worn when using post drivers (p35).

- Only trained operators should use powered equipment, including strimmers, brush cutters and chain saws. Training is available through BTCV, Lantra (p115) or local agricultural or land-based colleges.

- Attend to splinters promptly, taking particular care with the thorns of blackthorn, which are liable to cause infection.

- Take great care when lifting and handling heavy or awkward objects (see below).

- Clear up as you work, and don't leave cut material or debris littering the area.

TOOL USE

The following points are basic to all tool use. Further details are given where appropriate in later chapters. All tools must be properly maintained (p37). Any tools with loose heads, cracked or splintered handles or other defects should be repaired. See *Toolcare* (BTCV, 2000) for full details.

- Edged tools are safest when sharp. See page 37 for details on sharpening in the field.

- Carry edged tools at their point of balance, just below the heads, and positioned at your side with the edges pointing down and slightly away from you. Bowsaws should be carried with the blade protected by a plastic sleeve, or one made from sacking. Don't carry more tools than you can safely grip.

- If unfamiliar with a tool, don't use it until you have been shown the safest technique.

- Take great care with billhooks, slashers, axes and saws.

- Keep a safe distance from other workers, equivalent to at least twice the length of an arm and tool.

- When using a billhook, slasher or axe, always make sure there is a clear path to swing the tool. Even a small twig can deflect the tool and cause injury.

- Never cut towards yourself with an edged tool.

- When using a short-handled tool, keep your free hand away from the line of cutting.

- Don't leave tools lying around, as they are likely to cause injury, or get mislaid. Prop tools against a nearby tree or stump, or keep them together in a hessian sack or tool box. Store the tools centrally on the site so that all users know where to find and return them.

LIFTING AND HANDLING

- Before lifting and carrying, plan the route carefully, and clear it of any hazards which may trip people up.

- When moving heavy objects, particularly when working in a pair or team, think through the ergonomics of the situation, and plan your moves carefully.

- When lifting, bend your knees, not your back, and lift using your leg muscles.

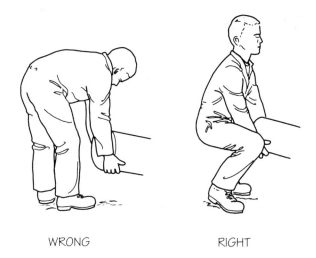

WRONG   RIGHT

- Be aware of your own and other people's physical limitations, and never try to lift more than you or others are capable of.

- Ensure you have a good grip on heavy or awkward objects, using the whole hand, not just the fingertips.

- Avoid manual handling where possible, by using wheelbarrows or machines.

Clothing

For work clothes, the aims are always safety and comfort. For general work you will need the following:

- Overalls, boilersuits or close-fitting work clothes. The wearing of loose clothes and scarves is dangerous when working with edged tools and among branches and brambles.

- Boots. Heavy leather work boots with deep moulded soles and safety toe caps, either external or internal, are best. In wet conditions, wellingtons with safety toe caps are recommended. Trainers, light shoes and normal wellingtons do not give adequate protection.

- Gloves. These are essential when dealing with brambles and thorns. Hedging gloves with gauntlets give extra protection against thorny scrub. For general work, suede palmed 'rigger' gloves are suitable. Gloves should not be worn when using edged tools, as the tool can easily slip. Criss cross 'gripper' gloves give improved grip.

- A safety helmet complying to EN 397 should be worn when using a post driver (see below). Working with chainsaws, brush cutters, near heavy machinery or working aloft, none of which are covered by this handbook, will require the wearing of helmets and other protective items.

Tools and accessories

Items are listed by category according to their most important type of use.

FOR ALL PROJECTS

A First Aid Kit, complying with current Health and Safety requirements, should be available at all times. For projects involving up to 10 people, the contents should be as follows:

1   guidance card

20   waterproof plasters

2   No. 16 sterile eye pads

6   triangular bandages

6   safety pins

6   medium sterile dressings 12 x 12cm

4   large sterile dressings 18 x 18cm

10   alcohol free cleansing wipes

2   pairs latex gloves

1   pair scissors, blunt-ended

The following welfare kit is also useful:

Pair of tweezers

Pair of scissors

Safety pins

Needle and thread

Pencil

Sanitary towels

Whistle

Toilet roll

Cotton wool

30 plasters

3 finger pouches

rubber gloves

insect repellent

2 x 10p pieces

sun cream

barrier cream

A list of local hospitals with casualty departments should also be to hand.

PLANTING AND EARLY CARE

Tree propagation

Garden roller, for preparing seedbeds

Garden rake

Hoe

Secateurs

Wheelbarrow, heavy-duty, with capacity of 0.08 cubic metre (3 cubic feet).

For further details, see chapter 5.

Planting equipment

Heavy duty treaded garden spade

Heavy duty garden fork

Junior garden spade, for use by children

Specialist tree planting spades are available as follows:

The Schlich spade and the Mansfield planting spade both have a ridge down the face of the spade which makes a hole to take the main tree roots.

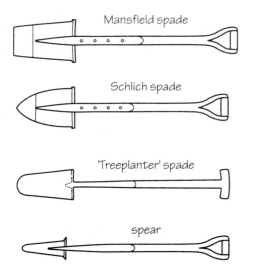

Treeplanter spades have slightly dished, treaded blades to make deep notches for planting transplants.

The treeplanter bar is a solid all-steel tool for planting in difficult conditions.

The spear is a tool designed for planting cell-grown plants. For details of use, see page 78.

A dibber can be used like a spear for planting out cell-grown plants in friable soil. It's also useful in a tree nursery for transplanting seedlings.

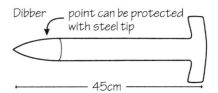

Marker canes or similar, to mark planting positions or lines.

Planting bags for carrying planting stock from the supply point to the planting position. Clean, heavy-duty plastic sacks are suitable, or specialist planting bags can be used for large-scale projects. Some growers of cell-grown plants can supply special carriers for use during planting operations.

Lump or sledgehammer, for treeshelter stakes.

Postdriver (Drivall), mell or maul for tree stakes.

Fencing tools

Fencing may be needed around tree nurseries or tree planting areas.

Crowbar, for making pilot holes for stakes.

Post driver (Drivall), mell or maul for driving posts.

Shuv-holer, for removing soil from post holes.

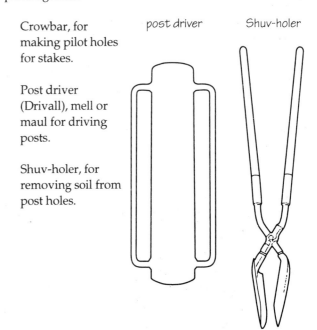

Wrecking bar (swan neck).

Claw hammer

Fencing pliers

Mallet and chisel

Wire strainers

Heavy-duty wire cutters

Tinsnips, for cutting netting.

Pruning tools

Secateurs. Bypass action type are recommended.

Loppers. Various grades are available for cutting branches up to 3 or 5cm (1 or 2") diameter.

Treetop pruner. Extension poles give 3m cutting reach, for high pruning or seed collection.

Pruning saw. Extension poles available for high pruning.

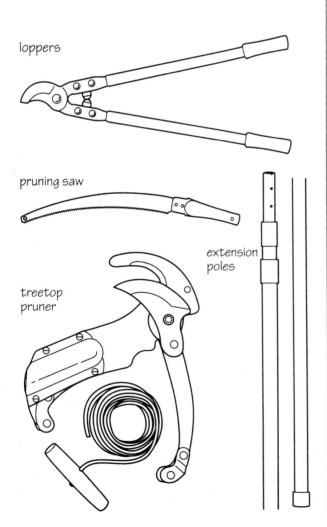

loppers

pruning saw

treetop pruner

extension poles

Easy reach tools

Several manufacturers produce tools to which optional longer handles can be attached to extend their use. These are ideal for weeding and other tree nursery work, especially for those people who find it hard to bend or who work from a wheelchair. Tools are available from Wolf, Spear and Jackson and other manufacturers.

Thrive (formerly Horticultural Therapy) offer a comprehensive information service on all aspects of gardening and horticulture for those with special needs (address on page 115).

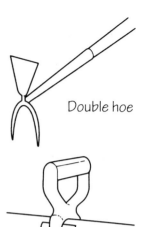

Double hoe

Auxiliary grip

CLEARANCE AND COPPICING

Clearing tools

Long handled scythe (Turk scythe) for cutting grassy rides and glades.

Grass hook, for cutting herbaceous material.

Brushing hook (slasher) for bramble and other light woody material.

Heavy-duty slasher for scrub clearance.

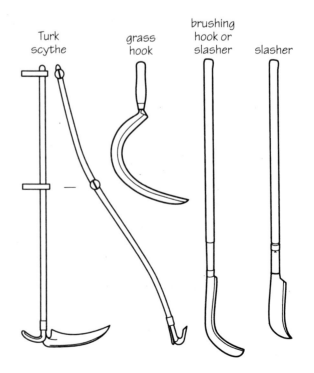

Turk scythe

grass hook

brushing hook or slasher

slasher

Coppicing

Billhook, for coppicing, clearance and hedge laying. Various patterns are available. A fairly light, single edged tool is suitable for most users.

BILLHOOKS

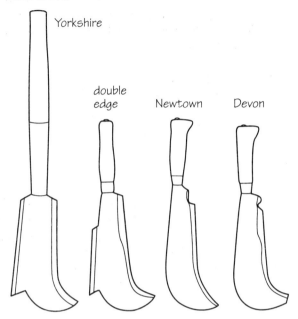

Yorkshire

double edge   Newtown   Devon

Bowsaw. The 53cm (21") bowsaw is suitable for most coppicing work, as its triangular shape makes it possible to use in confined spaces. Suitable for cutting wood up to 12.5cm (5") diameter. The 60cm (24") bowsaw is suitable for felling large coppice stems, small trees, and for cross-cutting felled timber.

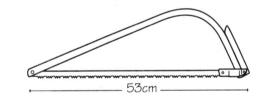

53cm

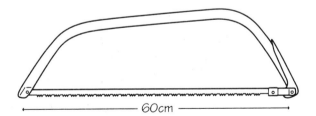

60cm

Clearing or snedding axe, for snedding, trimming and coppicing.

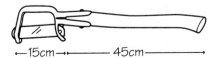

15cm   45cm

Sharpening stones

Tool and equipment maintenance

Proper maintenance of tools and equipment is essential for safe and efficient working. This section includes general points on storage, transport and care of tools, and techniques for sharpening tools in the field. Workshop tasks are described in *Toolcare* (BTCV, 2000).

STORAGE AND GENERAL CARE

- Keep all tools clean and dry. Carry a rag with you to wipe off the handles in wet weather. Keep edges free from mud, or they will dull very quickly. Clean tools immediately after use. If mud is left to harden, tools will be more difficult to clean and sharpen.

- Oil all metal parts before storing to prevent rust. Ordinary vegetable oil is suitable. Wipe unvarnished wooden handles with linseed oil when new and occasionally thereafter, as this helps keep them supple.

- If handles are rough or splintery, sand them smooth. Nicks in metal handles should be removed by filing.

- Store tools in a dry, well aired building, preferably in racks or on wall brackets. Keep similar tools together.

- Hang bowsaws with the blade tension released.

- Tools and equipment carried inside a passenger vehicle must be in secure containers fixed to the floor. Tools that will not fit into appropriate containers should be carried in a separate vehicle, or stowed securely in a trailer or on a roof rack. Edged tools should be protected with plastic guards, or with sacking or similar. In cars, tools should be transported in a boot, or covered hatchback area, preferably in a strong container.

SHARPENING EDGED TOOLS IN THE FIELD

- Edged tools should go into the field sharp. Major sharpening is a workshop task, and should not be attempted in the field.

- Sharpen tools at least twice a day when in use, or more often as necessary. Sickles and scythes need frequent honing to remain effective. Axes and billhooks should be checked whenever you stop to rest.

- Use the correct whetstone for sharpening each tool. Fine cylindrical (cigar-shaped) stones are used for sickles and scythes. Cylindrical or flat (canoe-shaped) stones can be used for billhooks and slashers. Axes are best sharpened with flat rectangular stones or round stones, fine one side, coarse on the other.

- Stones are fragile, and should be carefully stored and transported in a box or 'frog'. Broken stones are dangerous and should not be used.

- Always wear a glove on the hand holding the sharpening stone. Place the tool on a firm surface such as a stump, with the edge projecting, or sit down and steady the tool on your knees.

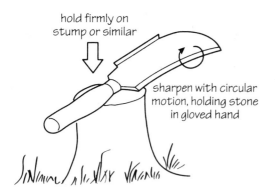

hold firmly on stump or similar

sharpen with circular motion, holding stone in gloved hand

- Moisten the stone with water, then hold it at the same angle as the existing taper of the blade. Avoid the temptation to use a wider angle to get an edge on the blade more quickly. With a combination stone, use the coarse side first to eliminate any flaws and bring to an edge, and then the fine side after to give an even taper and good polish. Sharpen with small circular motions, as this is safer than sweeping the stone along the edge, and is easier for the inexperienced worker.

- Take care to sharpen the hooked part of billhook and slasher blades, as this part of the blade does much of the cutting work.

- On single bevel tools, sharpen the bevelled side only. To finish, remove the burr on the flat side with a few light strokes.

- To check for sharpness, sight along the edge. You should see a uniform taper with no light reflected from the edge itself. Reflected light indicates a dull spot, so keep sharpening until this disappears. Don't touch the edge to check for sharpness.

SAW MAINTENANCE

- Oil blades frequently. When sawing through resinous trees, keep blades clean and free-cutting by dousing them with an oiling mixture of 7 parts paraffin, 2 parts white spirit and 1 part lubricating oil. Wear gloves to protect your hands.

- Change bowsaw blades when they are blunt or have lost their 'set'. Blunt blades take more effort to use than normal, and produce fine dust rather than crumbs or small chips of wood. Blunt blades are not worth resharpening, and should be removed from the saw and broken in half to avoid re-use. Take the pieces away for safe disposal.

- Blades can lose their set by being trapped in the felling cuts of trees, which gives the impression they are blunt. Reverse the blade in the saw (points into the bow), to make it easy to identify later. The set can be replaced in the workshop by gripping the blade in a vice, and then tweaking each tooth in turn to the correct side using a pair of fencing pliers.

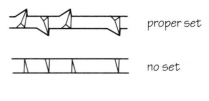

proper set

no set

Top view

- To change the saw blade, first release the tension. If this is hard to do by hand, put the saw on the ground with the frame upright and the blade pointing away from you, and pull back on the lever, using a metal bar if necessary. Then put your foot on the lever to hold it, and push the saw frame away from you.

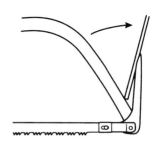

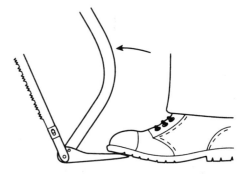

- Remove the rivets, position the new blade and then replace the rivets. Retension the blade by pressing the lever against the ground until it closes.

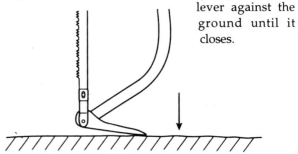

- If a bowsaw blade tends to 'run' (cut in a curve), reverse it in the frame. If this is ineffective, adjust the set on the 'gaining' side by running a whetstone once lightly along the blade, with the stone held flat against the blade.

- A bowsaw blade must be under high tension to cut straight. Increase the tension by fixing using the inner holes of the pair at each end of the blade. The frame can be 'opened' when held in a vice, to increase the blade tension.

Organising group work

These points are basic to organising group work. Further details are given where appropriate in the following chapters.

- The site manager or project leader should explain the purpose of the work, general site safety, demonstrate safe tool use and set the objectives for the day.

- Where possible, verbal explanations can be backed up with work plans, demonstrations or samples of work. For example, clear labelling of trees for planting and copies of planting plans will help avoid mistakes, and allow workers to get on without constantly asking for instructions. A tree library, consisting of marked twigs will help volunteers identify trees as they prune or thin.

- Small groups should work methodically on one goal at a time, rather than piecemeal on several things, none of which may get finished by the end of the day.

- Large groups should be divided up and work on several tasks or different parts of the site.

- Whatever the division of labour, don't leave anyone out, but find a place for people of all strengths and abilities. New volunteers can work alongside more experienced workers.

- Keep a close watch on tool use, and repeat earlier instructions as necessary. Don't hesitate to offer advice even to experienced volunteers, as otherwise new workers may follow poor practice. If a volunteer doesn't have enough skill for a job, tactfully suggest a change of tool or activity.

- Count out and count in the tools at the start and finish of work, and note any which need repair.

- In organising the group, aim for a balance between high work standards, and conditions which are not only safe but also rewarding for the volunteer.

5 Propagation

Propagation of native trees and shrubs from seed is not easy for all species, but by following the advice given below it is possible to grow your own planting stock from locally collected seed. General experience with growing garden plants from seed is useful, although tree and shrub seed requires some different techniques.

Note the following:

- The main benefit in growing your own plants from seed is that you can collect from local native trees and shrubs, which if growing in a similar soil and position to the planting site should be well adapted to local conditions. Very old trees or those from old woods or hedgerows may be of a local genetic strain which it is worth maintaining (p43).

- Growing your own trees from local seed is a worthwhile activity which can involve the community in many ways, and which not only produces trees, but has other benefits for the people involved. Growing trees from seed is an excellent project for schools, which has links with the national curriculum, as well as with wider environmental awareness and practical skills. Many schools have suitable sites for growing and planting, as well as the continuity required to maintain a project for a few years.

- A small, well-run nursery from which young transplants are produced for planting out may be worthwhile on economic grounds, as young trees can be produced very cheaply. On the other hand, commercial nurseries have the expertise and economies of scale to produce good quality stock at reasonable prices, and normally are able to give buyers the flexibility to choose what they want, when they want it. In your own nursery your stock will be limited by the seed which you are able to collect and successfully germinate, and grow on for two years. Trees of particular species do not produce seed every year.

- Local or community tree nurseries are likely to be most successful if they are set up in response to a particular need for planting in the following three or four years. Alternatively, they may be part of a large project where trees are to be planted each season over many years. The less successful community nurseries are those set up without a planned planting site for the stock produced, and where the temptation is then to keep the young trees for too long in the nursery. Record keeping is an important part of running a community nursery, as different people may be involved in running it.

- The Forest Reproductive Material Regulations 1977 control the marketing of reproductive material (seeds, plants and parts of plants) of species used for timber production, which includes five native species. These Regulations only apply to the marketing of reproductive material, and do not apply where planters collect and raise planting material for their own use. Since 1999, a voluntary system has been introduced which covers the sourcing, production and use of all native tree and shrub species throughout Britain. For details see the Forestry Commission Practice Note *Using Local Stock for Planting Native Trees and Shrubs* (August 1999), which should be consulted by all growers and planters of native stock, both professional and voluntary. It contains valuable guidance on the production and use of local stock of native trees and shrubs, including the map of local seed zones (p17), the native species appropriate to each zone (pp18-19), and advice on seed collection.

Technological advances

There have been many technological advances in the production and establishment of trees from seed. These make it easier, for the grower, both professional and amateur, to successfully produce and plant trees. For most species, this means that young trees can be planted out in their final sites within a period of about 2 years from the time the seed is collected. Short production times have obvious advantages for commercial growers, but for voluntary groups they are also appropriate. The shorter the time the young trees are in the nursery, the fewer the problems with control of root growth, disease and other factors, and the sooner the plants will be where you want them! Techniques include the following:

- Temperature treatment of seed, to encourage quick and even germination.

- Polytunnels and fleece, which give protection for young seedling trees, and allow the production of trees on nursery sites which might otherwise be too exposed or cold.

- Plastic netting, to keep birds off outdoor seedbeds.

- The use of plastic cells or pots for growing trees from seed until planting out.

- Plastic sacks for the safe transport and storage of young bare-root trees.

- The use of treeshelters and guards after planting out to enhance the growth of young trees, and to give protection from browsing animals.

- The use of herbicides or sheet mulches to remove weed growth around establishing trees. Herbicides or sheet mulches are a more efficient means of overcoming weed competition than the use of larger planting stock.

The simple guide

This chapter contains a lot of detailed information, which may be discouraging to the novice, and it is easy to lose sight of the fact that tree propagation can be as simple as putting an acorn in a pot. It is quite possible to produce young trees of many common species which can be successfully planted out in the autumn following seed collection. You may not be able to germinate all the species you want, but species which produce prolific and easy-to-germinate seed are by their nature 'pioneer' species which are ideal for starting a new piece of woodland. Alder, rowan, birch, ash and hawthorn should be easy to produce. Other species which produce seed less frequently or are more difficult to propagate, and which tend to be slower growing and shade bearing species, can be added to the woodland later.

- Collect seeds at the time given under the species details (p62), and either sow immediately in trays or pots of peat-free compost and place outdoors, or choose the simplest of the alternative methods given for pre-germination treatment (pp44-46). Protect from mice and birds.

- Sow remaining seeds (those given pre-germination treatment) in trays at the end of February. Keep moist, in greenhouse or cold frame.

- As soon as seedlings are large enough to handle (late March/early April), prick them out into individual deep pots or plug trays.

- Grow on outdoors in individual pots, or remove from plug trays when 3-4cm (1-1.5") high and plant out into a prepared nursery bed.

- Plant out pot-grown species in their final sites in September. Lift and plant out those from the nursery bed in late November.

- Protect from damage by animals and people, and keep weed-free for at least three years, until established.

Seed collection

WHICH TREES?

Sometimes you may want to collect seed from a particular individual tree, which perhaps has special historical significance or personal connections. Unusually prolific seeding of a particular tree or species may also be the spur to collection.

At other times you may want to collect a selection of species to produce stock for planting a new wood or hedgerow. Note the following:

- Contact the landowner to gain permission before you collect.

- In order to maintain local genetic stock, choose trees which, as far as you know, are least likely to have been planted. Trees which are obviously newly planted, for example along new roads, should be avoided. Also avoid collecting from woods which have trees in lines or remnants of planting patterns. Instead choose trees in old hedgerows, old woodlands, coppices or on common land.

- Choose groups of trees, rather than very isolated trees which are more likely to have infertile seeds.

- Within the guidelines above, choose trees nearest to the site you want to plant, as these are most likely to be of a genotype to suit local conditions.

- Avoid collecting from trees with obvious signs of disease, such as canker on the bark, or from deformed or stunted trees. However, some trees in exposed positions or on very poor soil may be stunted by the conditions, but the seed is still worth collecting, because such trees are likely to be from natural stock.

- Some of the smaller trees and shrubs are easy to spot and identify when in flower, but are less obvious at other times of year, including fruiting time. Keep a look out for species you want to propagate, and note their locations in readiness for collection time.

Note that trees do not produce seed every year. Different species have different average yearly intervals for producing a good seed crop (see species details, p62). Some individual trees tend to be good seed bearers, possibly due to genetic strain, site or other factors. Species such as beech and sweet chestnut may produce seed, but when the husk is opened the seed inside is shrivelled or absent. You will need to wait for a year when plump, viable seed is produced. Acorns and other large seeds can be checked for viability by putting them in a bucket of water. Viable seeds sink, non-viable seeds float.

Local provenance and origin

Provenance is a term used to describe the location of the group or 'stand' of trees from which reproductive material is collected. Provenance has been used for many years to describe particular strains of trees which are valued for their timber quality. Origin is a term used to describe the part of the natural range from which the reproductive material originally derived. However, as many stands of trees were themselves planted, their origin is not usually known. Reproductive material is considered to be of 'local provenance' if it is from stands of trees which appear well adapted to the location in which they are growing. Under the voluntary system outlined below, a Certificate of Local Provenance may be issued by the Forestry Commission to identify reproductive material which has been gathered and recorded following the procedures set out under the system.

Local seed zones

The 23 local seed zones in Britain are based on major geological and climatic variations (p17). Elevation, above and below 300m, is considered as an additional factor because of its important effect on local climate. From the approximate natural distribution of native trees and shrubs over recent centuries, a list has been compiled of the species which are thought to be native to each zone. A voluntary system is encouraging seed collectors, nurserymen and planters to follow these zones in matching seed sources to planting sites. In this way the local genetic stock of trees and shrubs in Britain can be perpetuated. For full details see Forestry Commission Practice Note *Using Local Stock for Planting Native Trees and Shrubs* (August 1999).

HOW TO COLLECT SEED

See the species details (p62) for the appropriate months to collect seeds.

Ordinary supermarket carrier bags are fine for collecting seeds, as long as they are kept in the bag for no more than a few hours. Otherwise, use buckets or hessian bags for collecting nuts and larger seeds which have wings. Smaller seeds can be collected in paper bags, envelopes or small hessian bags. Berries can be collected and kept for a few days in plastic bags as it does not matter if the flesh begins to rot.

Every bag or other container should be labelled with the species name, date of collection and location of the tree.

Secateurs or loppers are useful for clipping off bunches of seeds or terminal seed-bearing twigs. Long-handled pruners or treetop pruners (p36) enable the reaching and removal of seeds up to 3m (10') above ground level. Alternatively, a long pole with a hook can be improvised for pulling branches down to within reach. A step-ladder

may also be useful, but must only be used with at least one other person to steady it. Tree-climbing should not be used by non-specialists as a method of reaching seeds. When using long-handled pruners or long poles, take great care to avoid overhead power lines.

Seed can also be collected from the ground. Heavy seeds such as oak, sweet chestnut or beech can be picked up where they fall, or tarpaulins can be spread before the seeds fall to make gathering easier. The first fruits to fall are the empty and malformed fruits. The main seed fall will follow shortly after. You need to be prompt to collect before squirrels and other animals find them. Strong gales may bring down a large quantity of seed.

Where light seeds such as birch fall on hard surfaces they can be swept up and collected.

RECORDS

In addition to the labelling of seed, records can be kept of seed collecting operations in order to build up a picture of the most reliable seed trees in the area. Include the following:

• A map showing the exact location of the trees from which seed has been collected.

• A brief description of flowering and fruiting habits of each tree.

• The yield of processed seed from each tree.

• The growing performance of each seed lot collected, on a yearly basis.

Seed cleaning and storage

Remove damaged or shrivelled seed as you clean, as these are not worth storing or sowing.

SEED CLEANING

Seed cleaning is necessary for most seeds to:

• Extract seed from fruits for storage and sowing.

• Prevent seed going mouldy.

• Help reduce 'damping-off' or fungal contamination after germination.

• Allow the regulation of seed moisture content during storage and pretreatment.

Methods vary according to the type of fruit or seed.

Cones

Includes conifers, as well as alder and birch. Dry the cones indoors until they begin to open, and then place them in paper bags and shake to release the seeds.

Nuts

Species include oak, sweet chestnut and beech. Remove acorns from their cups, and remove chestnuts from their husks. Acorns collected from the ground should be checked carefully as they are often partially chewed. Discard any that are damaged.

Winged seeds

Species include ash and field maple. Remove from twigs and stalks, but leave wings intact.

Fleshy fruits

These include hips, haws and berries from species including crab apple, hawthorn, rowan and holly. These require cleaning in order to remove the flesh from the seed, as the flesh contains inhibitors to germination. In the wild, the flesh is removed as the seed is passed through the gut of birds and animals which eat the fruit. A cleaning process is required to imitate this, as follows:

1 Soaking or maceration will help soften the flesh, particularly of fruits which were not quite ripe at collection. Soak the fruit in buckets or other suitable containers, leaving them until they are soft, but not so long that they start to ferment, indicated by bubbles and smell.

2 With some fruit, the flesh and non-viable seeds will rise to the surface where they can be skimmed off, leaving the viable seeds at the bottom. Mashing with a stout pole, potato masher or similar will help to separate the flesh from the seed. Seeds can also be pressed through a sieve. Hawthorn and holly, which have very hard seeds, can be depulped in a food processor without risk of damaging the seed.

3 After depulping, thorough washing of the seed is needed to clean away all traces of the pulp. Washing under a fast jet of water is the best method.

STORAGE

Some species are best sown immediately in trays or pots. Other seeds should be stored until the correct time to start warm/cold treatment, in order to time germination for early spring.

Long-term storage may be needed where you have excess seed which you want to keep for future years, normally of species which only produce seed intermittently. The seed of most species, called orthodox seed, can be safely dried for storage. Orthodox seeds should be gently dried by spreading out on trays lined with kitchen paper or newspaper in a warm room. Put the clean, dry seed into poly bags, expel the air, label and seal securely. The bags can then be stored in a fridge at 2-5°C, for several years as required, and the seed will remain viable. When the seed is required, follow the recommended times for stratification or temperature treatment (see species details, p62), before sowing.

Recalcitrant seed, produced by oak, beech and the non-native chestnut, will be killed if dried. They should be stratified or sown within a few days of collection, to prevent moisture loss.

Breaking dormancy

Dormancy is a way that tree seed protects itself and remains alive until conditions are suitable for germination. If tree seeds germinated in autumn, the young seedlings would be damaged or killed by the conditions over winter. In natural conditions, the winter temperatures and high moisture in the seed help break dormancy. This can be imitated in the nursery by simply sowing seeds outdoors in autumn. However for most species, erratic germination and predation by birds and animals means this method is wasteful of time and space. Instead seed is stored over winter, but has to be given a similar temperature and moisture regime in order to break dormancy. This procedure is called pre-sowing treatment, or pretreatment.

In the past this was done by keeping the seed outdoors, as in natural conditions, but kept moist and protected from birds or animals by 'stratification' (see below). In most commercial nurseries this procedure has been superseded by chilling the moist seeds in fridges or cold stores. This gives better temperature and moisture control, better protection from pests, and allows the seed to be more easily checked as it approaches germination. It also permits an accelerated timescale, so for example an 18 month cold-warm-cold cycle can be reproduced in 6 months.

There is no one single method of pretreatment which is effective on all broadleaved tree species, and a variety of methods may be used. There are also alternative methods for most species, which can be used according to circumstance. Germination of all seeds in any batch, or 100% germination, is impossible; 70% is considered a success for most species. Details for each species are given in the species details(p62).

SHALLOW DORMANCY

Some seeds, including most conifers, alder and birch, have only shallow dormancy, and an acceptable rate of germination may be achieved by simply sowing the seed direct from storage into a seed tray, as with ordinary garden seeds from a packet. Seed is very plentiful, so a low germination rate is not a problem. For higher rates of germination, use either of the following methods:

1 Place some kitchen towel in the base of a tray, and moisten it.

2 Sow dry seeds on top of the kitchen towel, and then place the tray in a polythene bag to retain moisture.

3 Chill in fridge for 3-6 weeks.

4 Bring tray into room temperature, and keep it dark by covering with newspaper or similar until seeds germinate. Check daily.

5 As soon as the seeds germinate, carefully plant them out into individual rootrainers, cells or pots.

To treat larger quantities of seed by a similar method, put the seeds into a fine net bag, made from old tights or similar, and then put the bag with the seeds inside into a container and top it up with water. Chill the seeds in the fridge for 3-6 weeks, and then remove. The seeds will be a wet mass which cannot easily be sown, but you can then put the bag containing the seeds into a spin drier (not a tumble drier), and spin the seeds dry. They can then be spread onto moist kitchen paper at room temperature as above. Keep the seeds moist and dark until they germinate.

DEEP DORMANCY

Most broadleaved tree seeds are deeply dormant, and may have one or more of the following characteristics:

* A hard seed coat which prevents water uptake or prevents the root emerging.

* Seed coats may contain germination inhibitors.

* Embryos may be immature, and require time to mature within the seed coat.

Deep dormancy is broken by moisture, changing temperatures and time. This can be done by controlled temperature treatment, by stratification and/or scarification of hard seed coats by abrasion. The starting of these procedures must be timed so that seeds germinate in early spring, to have the benefit of a long growing season. A guide is given below, with further details of pretreatment periods given in the species details (p62), aimed at a sowing date of about 1 March.

CONTROLLED TEMPERATURE PRETREATMENT

There are four different combinations of temperature pretreatment. Warm pretreatment should be at 20°C, and chilling at 2-5°C. Details for each species are on pages 63-65.

* Chilling only (8-16 weeks). Begin in autumn/early winter.

* Short warm period (2-4 weeks), followed by chilling (12-20 weeks). Begin in late summer.

* Long warm period (8-16 weeks) followed by chilling (12-20 weeks). Begin in spring/summer.

* Very long warm period (40 weeks) followed by long chilling (at least 20 weeks). Begin in winter.

Chilling is most effective when seeds are chilled at the optimum moisture content – for broadleaves it is 40-60%. See Gordon, A G (1992) or Finch-Savage (1998) for details on testing moisture content.

The general procedure is as follows:

1 If the seed has been stored, it should first be soaked in water at 3-5°C for 48 hours. Change the water if it becomes discoloured during that time. Dry the seeds by draining in a sieve, air drying or by spin drying (see above), so they don't stick together.

2 Some seeds can be treated 'naked', that is without mixing in compost or another medium. Naked seeds need greater attention to ensure that moisture is kept high, by being regularly sprayed with water. It's normally easier to mix the seeds in a moist medium for the temperature treatment. Suitable mediums include half and half mixtures of peat, peat alternative or decomposed leaf litter, with a coarse material such as grit, horticultural perlite or vermiculite. Materials should normally be sterile, although there is evidence that with warm treatment, microbial and fungal activity helps break down hard seed coats.

3 Mix one volume of seed with 1-3 volumes of medium, and place in a labelled polythene bag or plastic box. Keep the container in the recommended temperature regime for the species. Chilling should be done in a fridge. Warming can be done on a shelf over a radiator or similar. Use a fridge and/or room thermometer to check that positions are suitable.

4 The seeds respire and require oxygen, so twice a week open the containers and mix the seeds thoroughly to aerate them. Remoisten as necessary with a gentle spray. Take care not to over moisten. If you can squeeze a drop out of the medium, it is moist enough. Remove any seeds that have gone mouldy.

5 As soon as seeds split or chit (begin to show a root), they must be removed and sown. Towards the end of the pretreatment period check the seeds every day. If this is not possible, sow the seeds just before the end of the treatment period, rather than risk leaving them too long. A problem is that not all the seeds of any one species or batch will chit at the same time. If stored naked, it is possible to remove chitted seeds by carefully sieving or floating the seeds, and returning the rest to cold treatment. The process is repeated until no more seeds germinate. Another technique is to wait until about 10% of the seeds germinate, which should indicate that the remaining seeds are close to germination.

STRATIFICATION

Use the following procedure:

1 Soak seeds as above, and mix with four times its weight of moist sand, which ensures that each seed is separated from any others.

2 Place in a labelled open container with drainage holes at the bottom, and protect from birds, mice and other small animals by covering with fine (6mm) wire mesh. Acorns attract mice, and it's safest to encase the pot in fine wire mesh. Plastic plant pots are suitable, or use plastic boxes or buckets with holes made in the bottom.

3 Place the containers in a shady place outdoors, or bury (plunge) in sand or gravel. Plunging maintains even cool temperatures and moisture levels. If plunged, make

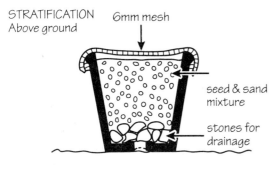

STRATIFICATION
Above ground

6mm mesh

seed & sand mixture

stones for drainage

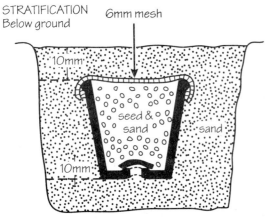

STRATIFICATION
Below ground

6mm mesh

10mm

seed & sand

sand

10mm

sure the pit is not liable to waterlogging.

4 Inspect the containers frequently as germination time approaches. Sow seeds as soon as they split or chit.

Sowing

The following methods can be used for sowing. They are described further below.

- Seeds can be sown direct into the container in which they will be grown on for up to a year. Suitable containers include rootrainers, cells and other narrow but deep pots. Acorns and other large seed can be sown singly. For medium or small seed, sow 4-5 or a small 'pinch' of seed and then thin as necessary to leave one seedling. Thinnings can be transplanted into pots where none have germinated. Do not sow direct into large containers as this is a waste of space, and the compost will go 'sour' before the roots have filled it.

- Medium or small sized seeds can be sown into trays or pots, from which they are transplanted or 'pricked out' shortly after germination, and grown on singly in containers, or spaced in trays for later planting out.

- All types of seed can be sown into outdoor seedbeds, and then thinned, undercut or transplanted (p52).

- Seeds can be sown direct into the place where you want the tree to grow. The ground must be clear of weeds, with the soil a good, friable texture. Sow several seeds at each position, and protect them from birds by covering the area with a fine wire or plastic mesh. In the spring, check frequently for germination. Mark the seedlings with a cane or similar so they don't get trodden on. Keep a 1m diameter area around the seedlings weed-free for at least three years. Thin as necessary to leave one tree by the end of the first growing season.

GENERAL SOWING INFORMATION

- Most seeds should be covered after sowing with a light covering of sand, fine grit or compost. This excludes light and helps maintain moisture around the seed. As a guide, the seed should be covered to the same depth as the size of the seed, measured on its longest axis. The smallest seeds are not covered.

- The pots or trays can then be covered with white polythene in order to keep them moist. If sown in spring or after stratification, check daily for germination. If outdoors, white polythene can be kept on for a few days to maintain high levels of moisture for the young seedlings, but keep a close look out for fungal diseases. In a polytunnel or greenhouse, remove the white polythene as soon as germination starts.

- Most tree seeds germinate best at temperatures below 20°C. Warm temperatures may reimpose dormancy.

- Seed which has been stratified or subjected to temperature treatment may have 'chitted' at the time of sowing. This means that the seed has swollen, begun to split, and the tip of the root or radicle may be just visible. Place seed carefully on the compost with the radicle pointing down, and thinly cover with compost. Provided you handle and grow them on carefully, you have a good chance of successfully growing on every chitted seed sown.

- When transplanting or 'pricking out' tiny seedlings, handle them carefully by the seed leaves. Don't pick them up by the stem, which is much too fragile for handling. Use the handle end of a spoon or fork to ease the young seedling out of the compost, and transplant immediately.

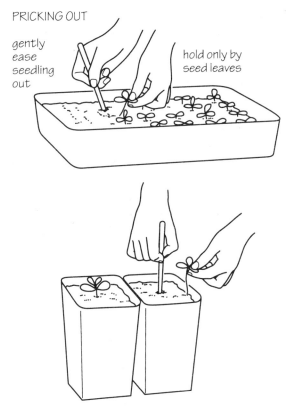

PRICKING OUT

gently ease seedling out

hold only by seed leaves

- Some species germinate erratically, so you may need to prick out seedlings as they appear, but then leave the pot or tray in cool moist conditions for other seeds to germinate.

- Germinating seed and young seedlings need protecting from birds, mice and other small animals. Outdoor beds are also vulnerable to disturbance by cats (p53).

SOWING IN CONTAINERS

Rootrainers, cells or other deep, square sided pots are the best containers to grow seedling trees. This is because the roots are encouraged to grow downwards, rather than spiralling around the pot. Once spiralled, the central part of the rootball stays this way after planting out and for the lifetime of the tree, and may contribute to instability in strong winds. The sides of rootrainers have vertical grooves to further encourage downward root growth.

Various sizes of rootrainers are available, designed for different species and types of plants. For broadleaved trees, the recommended sizes are as follows:

- Sherwood. Cell depth 12cm, cell volume 175cc. This is the smallest suitable size for most purposes. Most broadleaved species can be grown to a size for planting out in six months.

- Fleet A. Cell depth 17cm, cell volume 300cc, or Fleet B. Cell depth 20cm, cell volume 350cc. Suitable for growing seedlings on to larger sizes, for planting out on difficult sites. Also suitable for species which are sown in late summer, and therefore must spend a year in the container before they are planted out the following late summer.

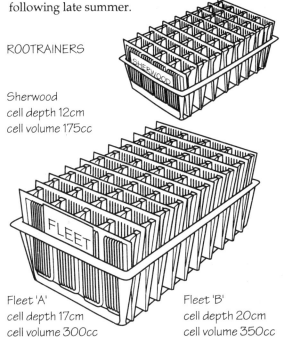

ROOTRAINERS

Sherwood
cell depth 12cm
cell volume 175cc

Fleet 'A'
cell depth 17cm
cell volume 300cc

Fleet 'B'
cell depth 20cm
cell volume 350cc

Rootrainers can be opened like a book, to allow inspection of the roots and to check that moisture is reaching through to the bottom of the plug.

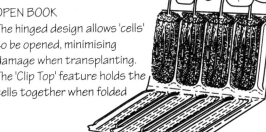

OPEN BOOK
The hinged design allows 'cells' to be opened, minimising damage when transplanting. The 'Clip Top' feature holds the cells together when folded

The rootrainers are held firmly in special trays. As seedlings develop, empty books can be used as spacers to give more room for top growth. Rootrainers and trays can be washed and reused many times.

If rootrainers or other commercial pots are not available, other deep square sided containers can be used. Orange juice or milk cartons with the base removed are suitable.

Small quantities of tree seedlings can be grown indoors on windowsills, in cool conservatories or greenhouses. Larger quantities should be grown in polytunnels. Consult a suitable reference book (Salt, undated) on the management of polytunnels.

All plants grown in protected conditions must be 'hardened off' (p50) before they are planted out.

Containers in greenhouses or polytunnels should be placed on a mesh rack or similar so there is an air space of at least 15cm (6") below them. This 'air-prunes' the roots, which means that root tips are dried off as they protrude out of the pot. This is beneficial, as it stimulates lateral rooting within the pot. If containers are placed directly onto the ground, the roots will emerge from the base of the pots and grow together in a mat, which makes planting out difficult and damaging to the plants.

ROOT DEVELOPMENT

| first root grows straight through drainage hole and dries off | lateral roots quickly grow out and down grooves, which prevent spiralling | the lateral roots grow through drainage hole and dry off, which promotes further root development |

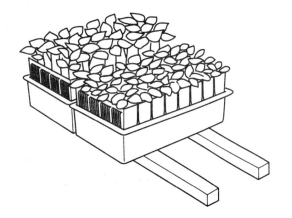

The simplest method is to raise the trays off the ground with timber battens. Simple benches can be made of concrete blocks and angle iron or similar.

Sowing medium

Seeds must not be sown into pots of ordinary garden soil, as this is too dense for young roots to easily penetrate, and becomes sticky or hard when watered. Sowing mediums or composts should have a high volume of air space, and be able to hold water without losing their structure. When removed from the cell prior to planting, the plug of roots and compost should hold together without crumbling, to avoid any damage to the roots.

Most commercial composts are based on peat, which is not an environmentally sound product, as it uses a non-renewable resource. Many alternatives are available, based on bark, wood fibre, coir, bracken and other materials. Coir is the residue from the processing of coconut husks for their fibre, and is imported from countries around the Indian Ocean. It can make good compost, but the environmental cost of transporting it should be taken into account. Locally produced composts from recycled waste wood products, for example composted ground bark, are probably the best product to look for. They can be used on their own, or mixed with peat to reduce overall peat use. This is a rapidly changing market, with new products becoming available each year. Many local authorities are now producing compost from recycled garden waste. Water authorities are also producing composts from sewage sludge and other recycled material. Contact them to find out what is available in your area. Compost suppliers are also listed in Yellow Pages. Some national suppliers are listed on p 119.

Many tree seedlings are sensitive to high alkalinity, and do best in a compost which has been formulated for ericaceous or acid-loving plants. A pH of 5.5 is recommended for broadleaved trees.

To mix your own compost, a recommended mix for the larger-size cells (volume over 175cc) is 70% medium coarse coir, with 30% ground composted bark. Alternatively, vermiculite can be substituted for bark, or a mixture of bark and vermiculite can be used. Coarse sand is often used in composts, but is not recommended for cell-grown trees, as more than about 2% sand will cause the plug to disintegrate when it is removed from the container.

Of home-produced composts, rotted leaf mould is the nearest to the sowing medium found in nature, and has the advantage of probably containing beneficial mycorrhiza (p70). Preferably use leaf mould collected from beneath the same species of tree that you are growing (p71). General garden compost may also be suitable. There should be no problems with weed seeds provided the compost has been well rotted at the high temperatures created in a compost heap. If weed seeds do emerge, they can be removed from the pot as soon as they germinate.

All composts should be moist, but not wet, before use. Rootrainers, cells or pots should be filled nearly to the brim, and then gently shaken to settle the compost into the bottom of the container. Do not fill to the brim, and brush off any surplus before sowing.

Additives

Fertiliser recommendations will vary between species, season and length of production. Commercial composts may already contain fertiliser and trace elements. If mixing your own compost, general recommendations for an NPK (nitrogen, phosphorus and potassium) fertiliser plus trace elements are as follows:

Mix with compost prior to sowing:
10%N + 10%P + 20%K – up to 2 litres/m³

During growing:
15%N + 15%P + 15%K – according to requirement

During hardening off:
10%N + 20%P + 20%K – according to requirement

In general, use less rather than more fertiliser. It is easy to scorch young plants with too much fertiliser, or too strong a solution. Slow release fertilisers, such as Osmocote, can be used but are not easy to spread evenly through small containers, because the granules are relatively large and sparsely distributed. Some cells may be missed out, resulting in uneven growth. Mix the granules very thoroughly, at the rate of 1-2g per litre of compost. Incorrect fertilising after mid-summer will keep the trees growing into autumn, and delay the onset of dormancy and the time of planting out.

Tree Growing Kits

These kits comprise 32 rootrainer cells with a holding tray and clear lid, and are supplied with coir, water retaining crystals, fertiliser, a growth chart and growing instructions. The lid doubles as a propagator lid and a tray for watering. They can be used to grow any species of trees or shrubs, and fit conveniently on a window sill for the early stages of growth. Watering from below, by using the tray or capillary matting, is recommended. Tree Growing Kits have been widely used by schools and other groups, especially in some of the Community Forest areas. With the addition of compost, the kit can be re-used many times. Tree Growing Kits are available from the Arid Lands Initiative (p119).

SOWING IN TRAYS

Seed which has not chitted, and very small seed, can be sown into trays of compost. As the seeds germinate, they need to be pricked out and transplanted one to a pot or other container. To sow a quantity of seed for pricking out, use seed trays or large, shallow pots, plastic boxes or similar, with drainage holes.

For small seeds, such as birch or rowan, take a pinch of seed and scatter it over the surface. Do not press it in or cover it with compost. Cover the seeds with a light covering of fine grit. Medium and large seeds can be placed on the surface of the compost, and then covered with a thin layer of compost. Cover the tray with white polythene, and proceed as described above.

DUNEMANN BOXES

'Dunemann' boxes, 'Kember' beds or similar containers are a useful method of propagating trees in small paved areas where no garden soil is available. Construct a bottomless, box-shaped structure about 1m (3') wide, 30cm (1') high, and of any length. Rough wood, old bricks or blocks can be used. It's useful if boxes are accessible with a wheelbarrow. Site the box either on gently sloping paving, or on freely draining, weed free soil. Avoid frosty sites.

Cover the base with a layer of clinker (the residue from burnt coal) and ash, or with coarse gravel and grit. Fill the box with well broken-down leaf litter, preferably collected from beneath the type of trees you want to propagate. Consolidate the leaf litter by trampling at intervals while the frame is being filled. Top with either of the layers shown below, to give a level, firm surface. Before sowing,

DUNEMANN BOX

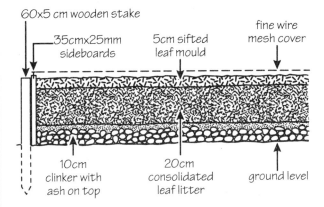

KEMBER BED

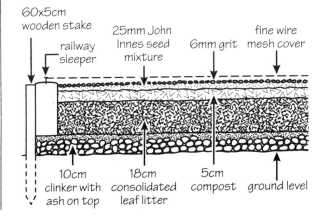

water the box well. Cover the seeds with 5mm of silt-free sand, and protect with 6mm wire mesh secured with a few nails or anchored with bricks. Ensure that the bed does not dry out by watering it from time to time. Additional boxes can be used for transplanting.

Growing on

CONTAINER-GROWN PLANTS

Once seeds have germinated, they must be moved into the light. For small quantities, a sunny windowsill, cool greenhouse, well-ventilated conservatory or cold frame is suitable. Take great care with watering, as each pot or cell must be watered separately, as there is no horizontal transfer of water between the cells. The outside cells dry out faster than the inner ones. Watering can be done from below, using a large tray or capillary matting, until the stage when the roots reach the bottom of the cell. Once they have reached that stage, the cells should be kept clear of the bench or ground, so that air pruning of the roots (see p48) can take place. Watering from above will then be necessary. Apply liquid feed regularly until mid summer, if not using a slow release fertiliser (see p49).

Polytunnels, glasshouses and other indoor environments must be kept cool and well ventilated. Polytunnels should have mesh sides to above the height of the benching, to provide side ventilation, with 'skirts' that can be lowered in cooler weather. The temperature of the compost in the containers must not rise above 30°C, nor go below 6°C.

The following table gives the Horticultural Trades Association guidelines for the minimum cell volume, height and root collar diameter for broadleaves, at the time of supply for planting out.

Table 5a: Guide to sizes of cell-grown broadleaves

	HEIGHT BAND (cm)			
	10-20	20-40	40-60	60-90
Min. cell volume (cc)	50	100	150	200
Min. root collar dia.-(mm)	4	4	6	8

Once plants have reached the desired size in mid to late summer they should be hardened off by moving them outside, or by lifting the sides of the polytunnel. Lower nutrients, cooler nights and shortening days encourage the plants to stop growing and to form a terminal bud. Woody plants require a certain amount of chilling over winter, in order to respond to rises in temperature the following spring. Leave the plants outside through the early autumn, but protect the roots from frost. The containers should be well watered before the onset of

freezing weather. Either bring the containers into a frost-free building, or protect the roots by plunging the containers into straw, compost or similar. Cover the tops with fleece during frosty spells.

IN OUTDOOR BEDS

Seeds sown direct in outdoor beds need thinning or transplanting. Seedlings grown in trays or pots can also be planted out for growing on to a larger size. This process is described below under 'Tree Nurseries'.

Tree nurseries

The traditional method of growing trees is in a tree nursery, which mainly comprises outdoor beds in which trees are grown for between 1 to 3 years, and sometimes longer. As required, the young trees are dug up in the late autumn, and sold as 'bare-root' stock. If properly protected in plastic sacks (p60), bare-root stock can last for some weeks out of the ground before being planted out in their final positions. Species which resent root disturbance, which include holly and most conifers, are grown in containers. A nursery may include a polytunnel for propagation and early growth in trays or cells, and may grow a mixture of outdoor or 'field grown' plants, and others which are grown and sold in rootrainers, cells or pots.

SELECTING AND PREPARING A NURSERY SITE

In looking for a site, choose one which is easily accessible because frequent care is needed. A site which is secure from vandalism is also important. Private gardens, school or hospital grounds or other supervised sites are best. Allotments are also suitable. The site will be needed for a minimum of three years, so make sure you have sufficient tenure. As shown in the example (p51), a small nursery plot can produce a large number of trees.

Site selection

- A suitable soil, which is workable in early spring, is vital. Heavy clay is difficult to work, but light sandy soils will dry out too quickly and are nutrient-poor. A light lime-free loam, of a good depth to retain moisture, is ideal.

- A slight slope ensures good drainage, which is essential. Avoid steep slopes, as the soil will wash away. Also avoid an easterly slope, as the morning sun can cause damage after a heavy frost. On dewy mornings, the early sun can also scorch the leaves of young seedlings. The best choice is a slight slope to the west or north, or failing this, level ground. The site must not be in a frost hollow.

- Shelter from the wind. Temporary screens of commercial windbreak material, hessian or similar may be needed. For the longer term, plant hedges for shelter.

- A water supply is necessary.

- See page 62 for notes on maintaining soil fertility.

The following diagram is of a 3 x 4m tree nursery suitable for managing by voluntary groups. The aim is to produce young trees which are ready for planting out after 2 years in the nursery (1 + 1), with a small proportion being grown on for another year (1 + 1 + 1). All the plants are transplanted each year, to encourage a good root:shoot ratio. This also allows annual incorporation of leaf mould or compost and thorough weeding of all the beds.

- Sow sufficient seed to produce 4-500 seedlings per year.

- Seedlings of most species should be 10-30cm high at the end of the first year, when they are transplanted or 'lined out'.

- Line out in transplant beds at spacing to suit species (Table 5c, p57). At the end of the second year, there should be about 350 plants at least 20-40cm high (1 + 1), ready for planting in final positions.

- Plants which are undersized or not required for planting out can be grown on for one more year (1 + 1 + 1).

Fencing

The area must be protected against deer, rabbits and dogs. The seedbeds also need protecting against cats, birds and small animals (p53). A fence which excludes rabbits and dogs can be made from 31mm gauge mesh, 1050mm high. The lower 15cm (6") is buried under the surface as shown, to discourage burrowing. Preferably use coated rabbit-proof netting, such as 'Sentinel Green', which is galvanised and then treated with an anti-corrosive coating. With uncoated galvanised wire, the zinc used in the galvanising eventually makes the soil toxic.

RABBIT FENCING

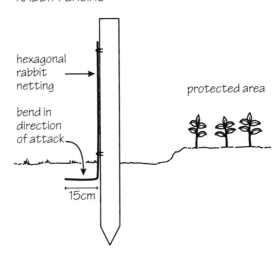

hexagonal rabbit netting

protected area

bend in direction of attack

15cm

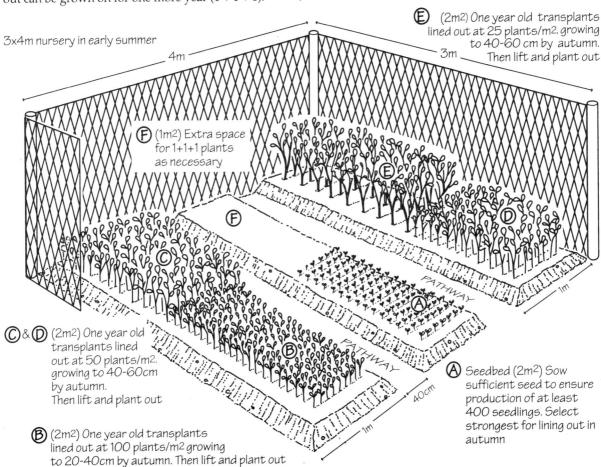

3x4m nursery in early summer

4m

3m

Ⓔ (2m2) One year old transplants lined out at 25 plants/m2, growing to 40-60 cm by autumn. Then lift and plant out

Ⓕ (1m2) Extra space for 1+1+1 plants as necessary

Ⓒ & Ⓓ (2m2) One year old transplants lined out at 50 plants/m2, growing to 40-60cm by autumn. Then lift and plant out

Ⓑ (2m2) One year old transplants lined out at 100 plants/m2 growing to 20-40cm by autumn. Then lift and plant out

PATHWAY

40cm

1m

1m

Ⓐ Seedbed (2m2) Sow sufficient seed to ensure production of at least 400 seedlings. Select strongest for lining out in autumn

Beds and paths

Seedbeds must be made afresh each year. In commercial nurseries, tractors with special cultivators are used which create raised beds, normally 1.1m (43") wide and about 10cm (4") high, with the tractor wheels making the paths or alleys between, which are about 50cm (18") wide. The soil in a raised bed is well drained and warms more quickly, promoting germination and growth. On sloping sites, run-off flows down the alleys, rather than washing through the beds. The beds are narrow enough to be hand-weeded from either side without treading on the beds. The sides of the beds tend to crumble during the season, so an 8cm (3") strip is left unsown along the edges.

In small nurseries, raised beds can be made by digging out the soil from the paths and using it to raise the soil level in the bed. The sides of the beds can be retained with planks of wood, or left as a bank. Beds retained with planks can be topped up with loam or compost as necessary, rather than being remade each year. Raised beds are essential for seed sowing, but on well drained sites with a natural deep loam, are not essential for the other beds, called transplant beds.

On a small site, mown grass paths are best avoided, as the grass competes for available moisture. If using grass, make the paths wide enough to mow, and don't have the young trees nearer than 15cm (6") to the edge of the grass. Alternatively use paving, old carpet, sheet mulch material or similar to make temporary surfaces to stop the paths getting muddy. These materials can be lifted when the raised beds are remade.

Clearance and cultivation

On heavy soils which have not been cultivated for some time, it's best to clear and dig in the autumn, to allow the winter frosts to break up the clods. Light loams can be dug on a dry day in late winter or early spring, so clearance, cultivation and preparation of the beds can be done in one operation.

If the area is short grass, cut and remove the turves. Stack unwanted turves upside down in a nearby corner, where they will rot down to a fine loam, which is ideal for creating seedbeds. If the area is rough grass, mowing at intervals during the summer to convert to shorter grass will make removal of turves easier. For rough growth, dig over the entire area and remove all top growth and roots. All perennial roots must be removed from the beds. A small piece of couch grass or bindweed, for example, can wreck a seedbed. Alternatively a herbicide can be used, but cultivation will still be needed.

Dig the entire area to a spade's depth. For heavy soils, fork over the bottom of each trench and leave the soil over the winter to weather. Mark out the beds, which are usually 1m (3') wide so they can be planted and weeded without trampling on them. Dig soil evenly from the paths and

throw it onto the beds, until the beds are 10-20cm (4-8") higher than the paths. Use planks as desired to surround the beds, secured into the ground with steel pins or wooden stobs.

Level out the surface of the beds and then firm them down by treading them with a 'shuffling' walk. Alternatively, use a thick plank and tread on it. The beds must be well consolidated before sowing to allow the soil moisture to reach the surface layers by capillary action, and prevent them from drying out in warm weather. A simple test is to press the bed firmly with the flattest part of a clenched fist. Consolidation is adequate when only a slight indentation can be made. Do not firm down the bed when the soil is too wet, or the soil structure will be damaged. The bed is now ready for sowing.

SOWING AND GROWING ON

As well as varying with species and strains, the size of seedlings at the end of the first growing season depends on various factors. The height depends on the sowing date, irrigation and whether they are grown under any form of covering. The stem diameter will increase with increased growing area, both above and below ground.

Sowing

Sowing is possible from early March to late April, depending on the area of the country, location and season. Delay the work if there is a cold, wet spell, and preferably sow on a dry, still day.

- Large seeds should be sown singly. Space acorns and sweet chestnuts 5cm (2") apart, and ash and beech 2.5cm (1") apart. Using a dibber (p35), make a hole twice the depth of the seed, sow, and then cover it with sieved soil or sand. Firmly compact to remove air pockets. Sow in rows to make it easier to spot the seedlings when they emerge. Protect with netting or fleece (p53), and use traps as necessary against mice.

- Acorns, beech and sweet chestnut can be sown in autumn. Temporary deep sowing is a traditional method for acorns, in order to protect them from mice and birds. Sow as described above, and then mark the top surface using a thin layer of sawdust, old plastic netting, strips of plastic sack or similar. Then cover this with an extra protective 10cm (4") layer of soil. Then in early spring, rake off the top 10cm (4") layer, and remove the plastic mesh or other marker.

- Large and small seeds can be sown in drills. Using the back of a rake or the edge of a board, make a 'valley' or drill to the appropriate depth, and about 10cm (4") apart. Sow the seed evenly along the drill, following the above spacings for large seed. Cover the drills with coarse sand or fine grit (see below).

- Normally, small seeds are broadcast by hand, trying to get as even a coverage as possible. Table 5c (p57) gives the recommended sowing rates for different species. Carefully weigh seed into small amounts, say 25g for the lighter seeds, and sow over the appropriate measured area. With experience, this can be done by eye. Very light seeds such as birch and alder can be mixed with damp sand to try and get a more even coverage. Birch, being a tiny winged seed, should be carefully sprinkled from just above the surface of the soil, rather than being thrown.

- After broadcast sowing, roll the bed with a garden roller to ensure good seed to soil contact.

- Immediately after broadcast sowing, thinly cover with a layer of sand or grit. This prevents small seeds from blowing away, excludes light and keeps the seeds and soil surface moist. Use pale, coarse sand, or grit which passes through a 3-5mm sieve, and cover to a depth so the seed is just hidden. Spread using a sieve or riddle to give even coverage. Don't use dark sand or grit, as this heats up in the sun and may damage the seedlings. Grit and sand must be lime free and silt free. Silt causes the grit to 'cake' or consolidate in rain. Fifty kg of grit covers about 4 square metres (92lbs covers 4 square yards). Don't economise by using soil for covering small seeds, as sand or grit give much better results. Birch is usually left uncovered as it needs light to germinate, but the seedbed must be kept moist.

Protection

Seeds, seedlings and transplants need protection from birds, small mammals and cats. Birds and mice may take the seed before it germinates. Acorns, chestnuts and beech nuts are especially attractive to large birds such as rooks, wood pigeons and pheasants, and may also be eaten by mice and squirrels. Moles can disturb seedbeds and transplant beds, and cats are attracted to bare, finely cultivated soil. Grit on the surface discourages cats and mice. Voles can damage seedlings and young trees.

Immediately after sowing, stretch plastic garden netting with a mesh size of 20 x 20mm over the beds to protect them from birds and cats. Suitable netting is available from garden centres and other horticultural suppliers. A width of about 1.5m (5') is suitable, and diamond-pattern netting

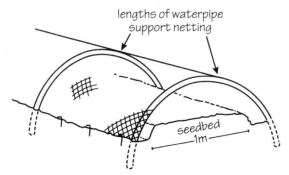
lengths of waterpipe support netting

seedbed 1m

which has some 'stretch' is easier to fit. Raise the netting off the ground, on hoops of 8 or 10 gauge galvanised wire or 20mm plastic water pipe or similar. The netting must be pinned securely to the ground all around, at intervals of about 45cm (18"). Pegs, similar to tent pegs, can be made from lengths of galvanised wire, or are available from garden netting suppliers (see p119).

Remove the netting once the first true leaves have developed.

Plastic netting is not proof against mice, voles or moles which can chew through or burrow underneath. Mice and voles are likely to be abundant where the seedbeds are close to hedges, long grass or other suitable habitat. Lay spring or 'humane' traps at intervals around the beds, baited with chocolate. Use mole traps set in runs as necessary.

Extra protection may be needed for autumn-sown acorns, chestnuts and beech nuts, which are very attractive to mice. You may need to envelope the seedbed with panels of wire mesh (6mm gauge). Before you make the seedbed, lay a piece of mesh to give about 20cm (8") soil coverage above. After sowing, cover the top with another piece of mesh and bend to close the sides. The top panel can be removed once the first true leaves have appeared. Sowing in protected pots or trays is another option.

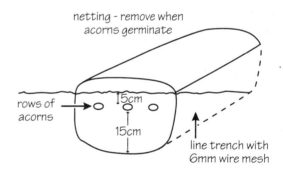
netting - remove when acorns germinate

rows of acorns → 15cm

15cm

line trench with 6mm wire mesh

As an alternative to netting, a 'floating mulch' or 'fleece' can be used, both as protection against birds, and to improve germination and growth rates. The fleece results in a higher soil and air temperature, higher relative humidity and soil moisture. Higher germination rates, faster growth and better one year seedlings are possible with most species, apart from beech, which is sensitive to higher temperatures. Fleece gives about 90% light transmission, allows natural ventilation and watering. It can be anchored by pegs, weights or by pinning to the surrounds of raised beds. Fleece is reusable if handled and stored carefully. Fleece should be removed once the seedlings start to lift it, as otherwise shoots can get entangled. For the first week or so after removal, replace at night or in cold or drying conditions, until the seedlings have hardened off.

Netting may be needed in addition for acorns and other large seed, as crows have been known to pierce the fleece in order to reach the seed.

Aftercare

Any weeds that appear in the seedbed are best removed by cutting through at just below ground level with a knife. If you pull them up, you may disturb the tree seeds and seedlings. Take great care not to mistake germinating trees for weeds. Weeding of newly germinating beds is best done by experienced workers.

Weeding must be done frequently, which means about every 2 weeks in spring and summer, and every month in the autumn and winter. Grass and other unwanted growth can appear at any time of year provided the weather is mild. Hoes can be used with care between rows of seedlings, but hand weeding is usually preferable.

Watering

Water the seedbeds whenever the soil begins to dry beneath the surface. Use a fine spray, preferably applied in the early evening. Avoid watering in bright sunlight, as the sun shining through the droplets can scorch the young leaves. Beds of birch or alder seed need to be kept moist throughout the germination and early seedling period.

DISEASES AND PESTS

There are several common diseases and insect pests which can cause damage to seedling trees. Larger pests are dealt with above under 'Protection'.

Damping off

This is caused by soil fungi, and can affect germinated seeds and young seedlings. Seedlings may fail to appear, or suddenly collapse. Damping off can occur in patches through the seedbed, or in pots or trays. Try and prevent it in polytunnels and greenhouses by good hygiene. This means cleaning benches, glass or polythene, cleaning pots after use, using clean soil-less composts and irrigating with clean water. Sow thinly, water sparingly and keep the tunnel well ventilated. Watering must be related to temperature, as excess moisture at low temperatures may cause the problem. As temperatures rise and growth increases, the volume of water applied can be increased. Established outbreaks cannot be controlled. As soon as you notice any signs of damping off, remove the affected seedlings and water the remainder with Cheshunt Compound.

Grey mould

Seedlings in greenhouses may be affected. Infected parts die back and give off a grey 'smoke' of spores when touched. Apply Captan immediately damage is seen, and then every 10 days until no mould is evident. Increase ventilation.

Mildew

This fungal disease can appear on two year old or older plants including oak, hawthorn and willow. It appears in warm dry weather, in April or May, when newly emerged leaves may be affected by spores produced from buds in which the fungus has overwintered. Pale brown spots appear on the undersides of leaves, from which a white mycelium spreads across the foliage. Avoid watering from above, but use capillary matting under pots or water outdoor beds with a seep hose. Diseased shoots should be cut off in the autumn to prevent the spores overwintering.

Chafers (Melolantha spp) and cutworms

The grubs of chafers feed on the roots of seedlings and transplants. Cutworms, which are the caterpillars of various moth species, gnaw at the root collars of seedlings, usually cutting them off at soil level. Apart from using insecticides, control of both pests can usually be achieved by regularly cultivating the soil and removing the grubs or caterpillars by hand.

Ants

Ants may sometimes cause problems in seed and transplant beds by taking seed, building nests and loosening the soil so that plants wilt and die. Use ant killer on the nests and runs. Some gardeners plant lavender as a deterrent to ants.

Transplanting in the nursery

By the end of the first year following germination in the spring, the seedlings of broadcast, small-seeded species will be crowded in the seedbed, and will need transplanting to give them more room to grow. Large seeded species, including oak, cherry and chestnut, which are spaced when sown, can be left in position for another year, and undercut (see below) to stimulate root growth, although transplanting is usually preferable in small nurseries. If more than 50% of the seedlings in a bed are less than 4cm (1.5") tall, they should be left to grow on for another year. This may happen due to late sowing or germination, or poor growing conditions.

The disturbance to the root system caused during transplanting, combined with root pruning as necessary (see below), stimulates the plant to grow more side roots so that a fibrous, bushy root system results, rather than fewer, deeper roots. This type of root system allows the plant to be dug up without too much root damage, and means it should successfully establish in its final position at the end of the second year. Transplants should have a high proportion of roots to shoots. They are described by their age and time of transplanting. For example, 1 + 1 denotes one year's growth in the seedbed, followed by transplanting in the first winter, followed by a year's growth in the transplant bed. The number denotes a year's growth, not necessarily a full calendar year. Seedlings grown in less favourable conditions may require 2 years in the seedbed, followed by one year in the transplant bed, denoted as 2 +1.

In commercial nurseries, additional methods are used to encourage root branching. These include undercutting (see below), side cutting and wrenching, all of which can be done during the growing season, as can transplanting. The main purpose of all these treatments is to encourage root development whilst effectively checking top growth. For further details see Morgan (Forestry Commission, 1999).

Transplanting or 'lining out' is normally done between October and April, depending on the season and location, with autumn preferable in most areas. Seedlings lined out in autumn are usually significantly larger at the end of the following growing season than seedlings lined out in spring. In the north and east, autumn transplanting may lead to transplants being lifted by frost action, so early spring transplanting may be preferred. Late spring transplanting disturbs early root growth, and plants will suffer if there is a late spring drought. An exception is holly, which is better transplanted in late spring, when the soil has warmed up.

The diagrams below show the sequence of growth from seed to 2 year old transplant. Note that the period of root inactivity is much shorter than the period of shoot inactivity. Tree roots continue to grow after leaf-fall until about mid December. Shortly before the buds open in spring, once the soil temperature exceeds 6°centigrade, there is a burst of root cell division and expansion which sustains the plant through the spring. Once the buds burst, root growth slows. Autumn transplanting allows the plant to maximise this important early spring root growth. The same applies to the final planting out.

LIFTING

Lifting and transplanting on the same day is preferable, as this lessens the chance of deterioration in storage. However, if transplanting on the same day is not possible, lifted seedlings can be stored as for final lifting (see below), and kept for a week or so if necessary. Cold storage is commonly used on commercial nurseries to give extra flexibility in management of stock.

If possible transplant on a still, damp day, as this will reduce the drying effect on exposed roots, and lessen the stress on the plants. Avoid working in very wet conditions or when the soil is waterlogged, as root damage is likely if plants are lifted with sticky clods of soil attached. Use the following procedure for transplanting:

- Always work from the outside of the bed. Insert a fork vertically to its full depth and then ease it forward to loosen the soil.

- Grasp the seedlings at ground level and lift gently, allowing excess soil to fall from the roots. The root hairs are very delicate. Don't shake the plants or knock them against the fork to remove the soil. The soil helps protect the root hairs and lessens water loss. If working on a windy, drying day, put the seedlings immediately into a plastic bag, close the top, and take them into a shed or other sheltered place to separate, root prune and sort.

- With sharp secateurs, cut any roots longer than about 15-18cm (6-7"), which can be a nuisance when replanting. Also prune any roots that are bent or twisted from growing in cramped conditions. Such roots will stay this way, and lessen the tree's chance of successful establishment. Root pruning stimulates side roots to grow, so encouraging the development of a bushy, fibrous root system.

THE GROWTH OF OAK

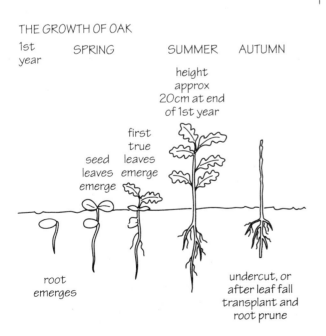

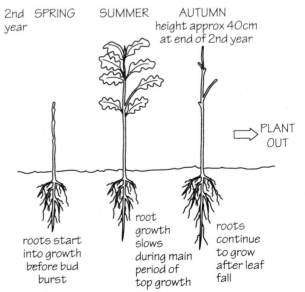

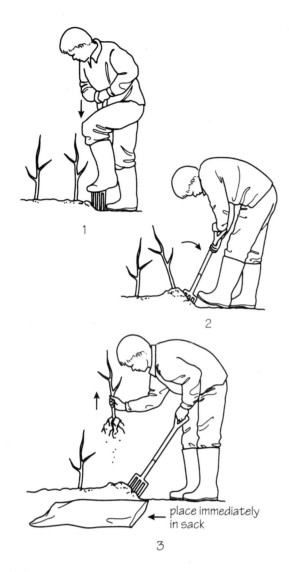

1

2

place immediately
in sack

3

- If there is a wide range in the height of the seedlings, then separate them into two size categories, and space them accordingly in the transplant lines. If mixed, larger seedlings will grow at the expense of smaller ones.

- The roots must be protected from drying at all times, so place the plants immediately into opaque polythene bags, and seal the tops. Keep the bags out of strong sunlight, and replant as soon as possible that day.

- Loss of moisture from the root hairs cannot be reversed by soaking the roots. This causes further damage by washing more soil from the roots.

LINING OUT

The amount which transplants grow in the nursery is related to the amount of space they are given. The greater the growing area, the sturdier the plant. A measurement of the root collar diameter (p56) is more significant than the height. Broadleaves for planting out in their final positions should have root collar diameters in the range shown below. This gives a guide to the size of stock you should be aiming to produce, for successful establishment.

Table 5b: Minimum root collar diameters (mm) for broadleaves: from BS 3936 (part 4)

SPECIES	HEIGHT (cm)				
	20	30	40	50	60
Birch	3	4	4.5	5.5	6.5
Beech	4	5	6	7.5	9
Oak, ash, cherry, lime	5	6.5	8	9.5	11

Growth rates in the nursery will vary with species, soils, location and weather. Growth rates also depend on the genetic strain of the seedling, and on use of fertiliser, management of disease and irrigation. In commercial nurseries, most operations are mechanised, so spacing will relate to the particular make or model of machinery in use.

In non-commercial nurseries, larger spacings are usually preferable. Crowded trees tend to be 'drawn up', with thin stems and poor root systems. Closely packed foliage also encourages the spread of mildew and other diseases. Weak, spindly or stunted trees are much more susceptible to disease than trees which are growing freely. Wider spacing may encourage more weed growth, but this is easier to hand weed than if the transplants are very closely spaced.

If space is limited, dispose of seedlings rather than crowd them. If you have far more than you are going to need in a year's time, it's better to dispose of the extra at the one year stage, rather than growing them on for another year or more, when you will find it even harder to throw them out!

The following table gives a guide to germination rates, sowing rates, seedling and distances for lining out (transplanting) at 1 year. There are no hard and fast rules about age for transplanting or lining out distances, which vary with different nurseries, areas, intended size at planting out, and personal preferences. Nurseries with less favourable growing conditions may grow seedlings for 2 years before lining out. The lining out rates suggested here are for non-commercial nurseries. In commercial nurseries the lining out rate is usually between 75 and 100 plants per square metre.

Lining out rates:

25 plants per sq m = 20 x 20 cm per plant
(rows 20 cm apart,
plants 20cm apart in the row)

50 plants per sq m = 20 x 10 cm per plant
(rows 20 cm apart,
plants 10 cm apart in the row)

100 plants per sq m = 10 x 10 cm per plant
(rows 10cm apart,
plants 10 cm apart in the row)

TABLE 5c: Guide to sowing and transplanting rates for native trees

SPECIES	Average % germination	Sowing: m². per 100g seed	Seedling height at 1 year (cm)	Lining out rate: plants per m²
alder	40	11.0	10-30	100
ash	60	1.8	10-30	50
beech	60	0.4	10-20	50
birch	30	22.0	10-30	100
cherry, wild	75	0.6	10-25	50
chestnut, horse	80	0.1	15-25	25
chestnut, sweet	80	0.1	10-30	25
elm, wych	45	7.0	10-20	50
hawthorn	60	0.9	10-30	50
hazel	70	0.2	10-15	50
holly*	80	3.0	5-15	–
hornbeam	45	1.2	5-10	100
lime, large leaved	70	0.5	10-20	50
lime, small leaved	70	2.2	10-20	50
maple, field	55	7.0	5-20	100
oak	80	0.1	10-20	50
rowan	70	9.0	10-25	50
Scots pine	85	9.0	5-10	100
spindle	70	4.8	10-15	50
sycamore	40	3.0	15-40	25
whitebeam	50	1.8	10-25	50
yew*	90	9.0	3-5	–

* container-grown species

Use a measured batten or similar for spacing, as growth will be more even, and weeding much easier, if the rows and spacing are precise.

Use a dibber or trowel to plant the trees, or alternatively dig out a trench and transplant as shown below. Make sure the stem is upright, or 'hockey stick' stems will develop as the stem straightens up with growth. The roots should be spread symmetrically downwards from the root collar. Never 'corkscrew' or bend the roots into too shallow or narrow a hole, as the roots will be permanently distorted. It's better to cut off a root that is too long, rather than bending it into a 'j' shape. Check the soil mark at the root collar to make sure you are transplanting to the correct depth.

Broadleaf P4 or Swellgel water-storing granules can be added at transplanting. When the tree is finally planted out, the clump of roots and water-storing granules gives the tree a good start. The granules not only release water as needed, but improve nutrient availability, and help aerate heavy or compacted soils. In addition, Broadleaf Root Dip can be used at final lifting (p 59), or granules can be added at final planting (p70).

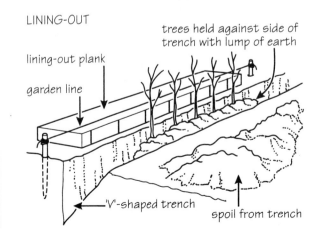

LINING-OUT

lining-out plank

garden line

trees held against side of trench with lump of earth

'V'-shaped trench

spoil from trench

UNDERCUTTING

Undercutting is used to root prune without lifting the plant. This technique cuts through any long roots and stimulates the growth of a bushy root system near the soil surface which can easily be lifted for final transplanting. For undercutting in commercial nurseries, seeds are precision sown at about a quarter the density of conventional seedbeds, and undercutting is done by a tractor with a buried horizontal blade, to produce uniform results. In a small-scale nursery, undercutting may be suitable for oaks, chestnuts and cherries, which are widely spaced when sown and thus do not need spacing out by transplanting in the first winter. However, undercutting with a spade is often difficult to do without trampling on neighbouring plants, and transplanting is usually the better method for small nurseries as it combines root pruning, culling of poor seedlings and respacing.

In commercial nurseries, plants may also be 'wrenched' whilst remaining in the ground, which also stimulates the production of fine roots nearer the surface. This can be beneficial for broadleaves which produce substantial tap roots, including oak and ash. Wrenching regimes can be complex and are only suitable for commercial production.

To undercut, a spade can be used as shown below. Undercut in late winter, a few weeks before bud-burst. Undercutting can also be done in the growing season, but extra watering and feeding will be needed for the next few weeks, while the plants put on new root growth. Don't undercut at the end of the growing season, in an attempt to convert long-rooted plants into suitable stock for planting out, as the plants will not have time to make sufficient new fibrous roots before they are lifted.

Push the spade under the plants as shown below. Make sure you cut to the depth shown. Practise as necessary in a spare piece of ground to get the correct angle.

UNDERCUTTING

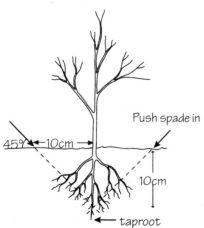

Push spade in

45°— 10cm

10cm

taproot

Lift the plants slightly before removing the spade.

Lifting for final planting

LENGTH OF TIME IN NURSERY

Ideally, a tree nursery should contain no native deciduous broadleaves older than 2 years, as this is the optimum age for planting out to ensure quick and successful establishment. On sites where growth is slower, 3 years growth (2 + 1) may be necessary. Any trees older than this are effectively being checked in their growth, and the longer they are grown in the nursery, the greater the problems of establishment when finally planted out (p67). Each extra year spent in the nursery also takes up an increasing amount of space, and requires additional work of weeding, watering, transplanting and so on.

In practice, the vagaries of seed supply, germination and the demand for trees will mean that it is very difficult to use every tree at the optimum time, and some further growing on in the nursery is almost inevitable if you want to have a range of species available for planting most years. However, there is a time to cut one's losses, and any broadleaved trees older than 4 years that cannot be found homes are best dug up and disposed of.

Yew and juniper, and the broadleaved evergreen holly are best grown in containers, and planted out when 2-3 years old. Scots pine can be lifted bare-root, as for broadleaves.

PLANT DORMANCY

Plants are most tolerant to the stresses caused by lifting, handling, storage and transporting when they are fully dormant. Dormancy is indicated when plants have stopped growing, and next year's buds have hardened or 'set'. Leaf fall occurs with most species, but not all. The most accurate way of testing for dormancy is to carry out a physiological test of plant dormancy status, which may be used in commercial nurseries to indicate safe lifting dates. For details see *Forest Tree Seedlings* (Morgan, Forestry Commission, 1999).

The onset of dormancy is influenced by seed origin, nursery treatments and seasonal conditions. Undercutting and wrenching both induce dormancy, while fertilising prolongs plant growth. Plants become dormant earlier in the north of Britain than in the south because of cooler temperatures. Dormancy, and hence lifting dates may be brought forward or delayed, depending on the prevailing climatic conditions.

Shoots become dormant in response to day length and air temperature, while root activity is affected by soil temperature and soil moisture. Roots can continue to grow for up to one month after shoot growth has stopped and buds have set. In Britain it is rare for shoots and roots to be fully dormant before the beginning of December.

Release from dormancy, or dehardening, follows a period of exposure to cold temperatures during winter. This chilling requirement differs between species and seed origins. Plants take less time to break bud the longer they have been exposed to low temperatures. Trees only begin to grow when dormancy is released and temperatures increase during the spring.

The ideal 'window' for lifting and planting out may be very short, according to the time of dormancy, bottlenecks in supply, available labour for lifting and planting, the short daylight hours in winter, and other factors. Climate change is delaying the onset of dormancy and bringing forward the date of bud burst, but is allowing more planting to take place in December and January, which used to be too wet or frosty.

The following table, based on information in *Forest Tree Seedlings* (Morgan, Forestry Commission,1999), gives a guide to the best lifting and planting out dates for bare-root broadleaved trees.

LIFTING AND TRANSPORTING

Follow the instructions for lifting and transplanting (p55). Note the following:

- Damage roots as little as possible.

- Don't work in wet or waterlogged conditions, as if the plants are stored wet in sacks, mould may develop on the shoots. The roots should not be stored with large clods of wet soil attached, as this can physically damage the roots and restrict their oxygen supply.

- Allow excess soil to drop off, but do not shake or knock the plants to remove more.

- Place plants immediately in a special plastic sack (for supplier see p119), which is white on the outside and black inside, and seal the top as soon as the sack is full.

- Handle the sacks gently, and do not throw, drop or stack them.

- Store temporarily in a cool, shady place, between 0 and 5°C. Do not allow them to heat up in sunlight.

- Store upright, not piled up on each other.

- Plant out in final site as soon as possible.

- If immediate planting is not possible, plants stored as noted above will not deteriorate if stored for a few weeks.

- Root dips, such as Broadleaf Root Dip, may help reduce root desiccation and improve planting out success.

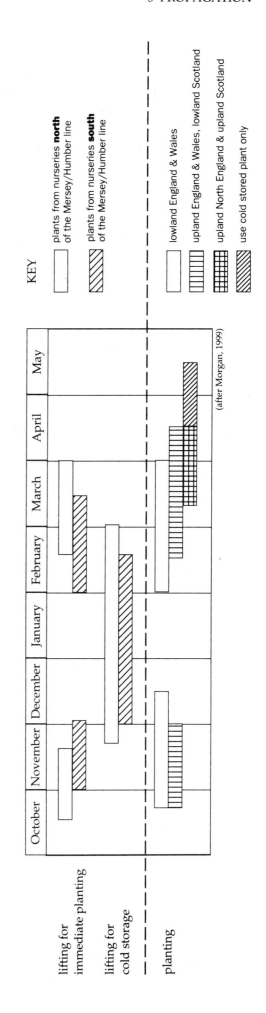

Table 5d Broadleaved trees – best lifting and planting times for bare-root stock

(after Morgan, 1999)

Heeling in

As necessary, heeling in can be used in order to free ground in the nursery for transplanting younger stock. The plants can be lifted in late October when the dying foliage is still attached, but before the onset of full dormancy. Plants will undergo the normal changes in dormancy during the heeling in period. This also allows the foliage to drop off before the plants are packed in sacks, to avoid problems with mould.

Choose a part of the nursery which has light, freely draining soil. Heavy, waterlogged soil will damage the roots. Never use water-filled ditches or similar for heeling in. Trenches should be dug as shown to the correct depth for the root system, and with a sloping back. Good soil to root contact is very important, as air spaces will cause the roots to dry out. Plants can be heeled in singly, or in loose bundles. If using bundles, make sure that the soil trickles through into the centre of the bundle. See diagram on page 72.

Packing in sacks

Bare-root trees lose moisture through the shoots, even if the roots are wrapped, so this type of packing is only suitable if plants are being immediately delivered and planted. Otherwise, all bare-root stock should be packed and transported in sealed plastic sacks large enough to include the whole plant. If plants are too large for the sack, invert another sack over the shoots and seal to join the two sacks. Clean, thick black plastic sacks are okay for storage for 24 hours or so, but for longer periods, use special co-extruded planting sacks which are white on the outside and black on the inside, to prevent the plants from heating up.

Aim to sort and pack the plants so that the sacks don't have to be re-opened until immediately before planting. Immediately after lifting, put the unsorted plants straight into plastic sacks and take them to a cool shed for sorting. Sorting in a cool, still, moist environment, rather than outside in the sun and wind, lessens the damage to the roots.

- Discard all diseased, spindly or damaged plants, or those with inadequate root systems.

- Cut roots longer than 15-17.5 cm (6-7") long.

- Quickly bundle and tie the plants into bundles of 5 or 10, according to plant size. Tie loosely with soft string, as tight rough bindings will damage the soft bark. Attach a label to each bundle, showing the number and species.

- Put one or more bundles into the sack, with the shoots facing upwards.

- Gently squeeze the sack to expel excess air, and then seal the top by folding it over and taping it. Label the sack.

- Handle the sacks carefully. Do not throw, drop or trample them, or stack them in piles. Store them carefully in an upright position, but not jammed tightly together. Tape over any tears or holes that occur.

- Store the sacks in a cool position out of the sunlight. For storage (fully dormant plants) for up to three weeks, use an unheated shaded building in which the temperature fluctuates as little as possible. Cold storage at +2°, or freezer storage at -2° is used in commercial nurseries.

- Keep sacks cool during transport. If stacking is essential to transport the plants, lay the sacks flat and stack no more than four sacks high.

Vegetative propagation

Vegetative propagation by suckers, cuttings or layers is used for some species. These include the following:

Table 5e: Table of species and possible methods of vegetative propagation

C = cuttings L = layers S = suckers	C	L	S
alder (Alnus glutinosa)	C		
aspen (Populus tremula)			S
beech (Fagus sylvatica)		L	
blackthorn (Prunus spinosa)			S
bramble (Rubus spp)		L	
dogwood (Cornus sanguinea)	C		S
elder (Sambucus nigra)	C		
elms (Ulmus spp)			S
guelder rose (Viburnum opulus)		L	
hazel (Corylus avellana)	C	L	
holly (Ilex aquifolium)	C	L	
honeysuckle (Lonicera periclymenum)	C	L	
hornbeam (Carpinus betulus)		L	
ivy (Hedera helix)	C		
pear, Wild (Pyrus communis)			S
poplar, Black (Populus nigra)	C		
poplar, Grey (Populus canescens)	C		S
privet, Wild (Ligustrum vulgare)	C	L	S
wayfaring tree (Viburnum lantana)		L	
willow (Salix spp)	C		

- Species which rarely set viable seed in this country

- Particular cultivars of species whose characteristics can only be maintained by vegetative reproduction.

- Species which are easier and quicker to propagate vegetatively.

SUCKERS

Some trees and roots have shallow roots which produce separate plants, called suckers. These can be separated from the parent tree by cutting through the roots around the sucker. It's easier to take small suckers, under about 60cm (2ft), than to attempt to detach larger plants. Keep the plant roots moist and follow standard planting advice (chapter 6).

HARDWOOD CUTTINGS

These are taken from wood that is fully matured, or hard. Species that can be easily propagated from hardwood cuttings include willow, poplars (other than aspen), dogwood, hazel, honeysuckle and elder.

1 Take cuttings from mid-October to December. From the previous season's growth, choose well-ripened dormant shoots with nodes, which are the swellings that mark the position of buds. Avoid shoots that are 'blind', or

HEELED CUTTING

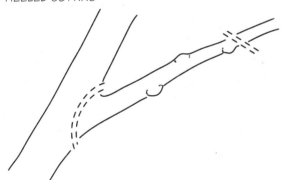

UNHEELED CUTTING

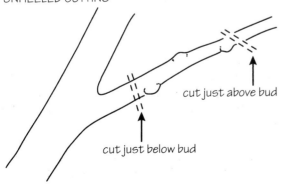

cut just above bud

cut just below bud

lack buds. Cuttings should be at least as thick as a pencil, although willow cuttings can be thinner. Some plants root better if they are taken with a heel. Poplar and willow should be unheeled.

2 Cut the shoots into sections 15-30 cm (6-12") long, with at least three buds to each section. Make the top cut sloping, at 3cm (1") or less above the top bud, and the lower cut straight across just below the bottom bud. The sloping cut allows water to run off. Unless the cutting is left with a heel, make the cuts as clean as possible using bypass secateurs, with the blade side on that of the cutting, so that the waste, not the cutting, is bruised.

3 Choose a site in the nursery which is sheltered from cold winds, preferably in a sunny, south facing situation where the soil will warm up quickly in spring. The soil must be well-drained, or the cuttings will rot. Drainage can be improved by placing coarse sand in the base of the V-trench before the cuttings are inserted. If conditions are very poor, with frozen or wet ground, the cuttings can be sealed in a plastic sack and stored at about 4.5°C in a shed or garage for a few weeks.

4 Space the cuttings 30-37cm (12-15") apart, in rows 37-45cm (15-18") apart, inserted to about two-thirds of their length. Tread well round the stems to firm the soil. Check at intervals to make sure cuttings are still firm, and have not been lifted by frost.

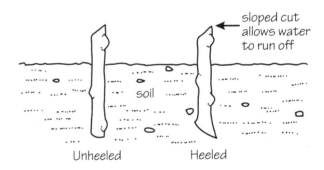

sloped cut allows water to run off

soil

Unheeled   Heeled

Cuttings inserted up to 2/3 length in the soil

Plants should be ready for transplanting to their final planting position at the end of the second growing season.

5 Cuttings of honeysuckle are best rooted direct into containers of compost and sharp sand or perlite. Provide a cane for support. Growth should be rapid, and plants can be planted out after a year.

The following points apply to poplar and willow cuttings only:

6 By late spring, the cuttings will have produced two or more sprouts at least 15cm (6") long. Cut off all but the strongest sprout on each plant.

7 At the end of the first growing season, cut the plant back to 3cm (1") above ground level to promote a better root:shoot ratio. Leave at least one bud on the stem.

8 Transplant to final positions at the end of the second growing season.

DIRECT PLANTING OF WILLOWS AND POPLARS

Willows and poplars root easily from cuttings, which can be inserted direct into the final planting position. Take cuttings from vigorous one-year-old shoots, preferably from coppice growth. Cuttings from mature trees do not root so quickly. The cuttings should be 20-25cm (8-10") long, with the top cut made about 1cm (half an inch) above a bud, and the bottom end just below a bud. 'Sets' are cuttings about 2m (6') long, taken from one- or two-year-old wood, used in the commercial planting of willows and poplars for timber, but all cuttings of willow and poplar for direct planting are commonly referred to as sets.

Cuttings or sets must have good contact with the soil in order to root well. In deep, cultivated soil, the cuttings or sets can simply be pushed into the soil, leaving about one-third protruding. In heavier soils this would damage the cuttings, and you will need to make a hole with a crowbar or similar. Depending on the size of the tool, you may need to backfill the hole with friable soil or sand to make sure there is no air pocket around the cutting. Note that cuttings and sets should receive the same attention to weeding as rooted plants (chapter 7).

LAYERING

Some shrubs (see Table 5e, p60) spread by side shoots which bend down and root where they touch the ground, forming a new but still connected plant. These species can be layered by pegging a shoot to the bare ground and covering it with soil. Once the shoot has rooted it can be separated from the parent plant by cutting through the shoot. The layer is then left for another season to establish itself before being transplanted.

NURSERY SOIL FERTILITY

It's important that the structure, organic content and fertility of the nursery soil is maintained if trees are going to be grown on the same site for many years.

Nursery soils must be light for ease of working, but this means they are hungry soils. Regular addition of organic matter will help maintain fertility and moisture-holding ability.

Good structure is maintained by avoiding cultivation in wet weather, and avoiding the trampling of beds. The addition of organic matter in the form of leaf mould, compost or well rotted farmyard manure will help maintain structure and water holding ability, as well as contributing to fertility. Avoid the use of peat. Organic matter can be added in the autumn or spring, when the beds are cultivated. A mulch spread over the transplant beds will help retain moisture and keep down weeds, and will become incorporated into the soil during the season.

Tree nursery soils must contain sufficient nutrients including nitrogen (N), phosphorus (P), potassium (K), magnesium (Mg), calcium (Ca) and sulphur (S). For most species, a soil pH in the range 5.5 to 7pH is suitable. Soil testing kits for pH and N, P and K are available from garden centres. Soils can be made more acidic by the addition of sulphur chips, which are available from garden centres.

Most commercial nurseries use inorganic fertilisers, in the form of soil dressings or liquid fertilisers applied to the trees in growth. For full details, see *Forest Nursery Practice* (Forestry Commission, 1994).

Species details

The following section contains details on seed collection, storage, pre-sowing treatment and sowing for different species of native trees and shrubs.

Note the following points, on which further details are given as indicated:

- Trees do not produce good seed every year, so you may wish to store seeds from good years. Storage for several years is possible for small seeds, but large seeds including acorns, chestnuts and beech nuts must not be allowed to dry out, and must be sown by the following spring.

- All seeds are vulnerable to being eaten by birds, mice and other animals. For storage, use airtight containers for small, dry seed. Hang large seeds up in hessian bags, suspended where mice cannot reach them.

- Fleshy seeds need maceration (soaking) after collection, to separate seed from flesh (p44).

- Stratification is a method of breaking dormancy by storing seeds outside where they are subjected to a period of chilling (p46).

- Controlled temperature treatment is a method of breaking dormancy by storing seeds in warm (20°C) and/or cold (2-5°C) conditions (p45). Seeds are treated either 'naked', or mixed with compost or other medium (p45).

- The pretreatment details given below are for a sowing date of 1 March, unless otherwise indicated.

TREES

Alder (*Alnus glutinosa*)

- Good seed crops every 2-3 years

- Pick ripe cones from September onwards, when the cones start opening. Cones may be gathered until spring.

- If cones are not open, they can be dried in a warm room. Then shake the cones in a bag to release the seeds. Separate the seed from the cones using a sieve. Store the seed in a cool dry place in a hessian bag. Don't store seed in a plastic bag.

- Sow in spring.

- OR use 'shallow dormancy' method (p44).

Ash (*Fraxinus excelsior*)

- Good seed crops every 3-5 years.

- Pick from August to January. If picked green in August, seeds can be sown immediately. Some will germinate straightaway, with sporadic germination the next spring. If picked from October onwards when fully ripe, stratification or temperature treatment will be needed.

- Do not remove seed from wing.

- Store fully ripe seeds by stratifying in sand for 16-18 months.

- OR mix in a medium, and store warm for 8-12 weeks, then chill for 8-12 weeks.

- Sow temperature-treated seed in the following March/April, or stratified seed in March/April of the second year after collection.

- Sow singly in pots, or spaced in trays for pricking out. Lightly cover with compost and keep moist.

- OR sow outdoors in a prepared seedbed.

Aspen (*Populus tremula*)

- Propagate by suckers (p61), or by softwood cuttings, taken in June/July. Choose vigorous shoot tips about 13cm (5") long, and insert into pots of compost of equal parts peat, coarse sand and sterilised loam. Keep in poly bags until rooted.

Beech (*Fagus sylvatica*)

- Good seed crops every 3-5 years.

- Collect seeds in September or November. Check for fertility by putting them into water. Infertile seeds will float to the top.

- Can be sown immediately in pots, trays or well-drained outdoor beds.

- OR store by stratifying outdoors, protected from predators.

- OR chill naked for 12-16 weeks. Spray regularly.

- Sow in March, in pots or trays, or outdoors in a seedbed.

Birch (*Betulus pendula*)

- Good seed crops every 1-3 years.

- Pick the catkins from August onwards, when they are dry and about to disintegrate. The catkins will fall apart releasing the seeds and scales. Store the seeds and scales in a hessian sack hung up in a cool airy room, and shake regularly to encourage air circulation.

- OR sow immediately in pots, trays or outdoor seedbeds. Sprinkle seed thinly on surface. Cover with a very thin layer of sand to help keep the surface moist, but not so much that light is excluded. Keep moist during germination and for 2 weeks afterwards.

- OR stratify outdoors for 6 months or until spring.

- OR store and then chill naked for 4 weeks before sowing.

- OR use 'shallow dormancy' method (p44).

Cherry, wild (*Prunus avium*)

- Small quantities can be propagated by removing suckers from existing trees.

- Good seed crops every 1-3 years, on groups of trees which have been cross-pollinated. Single trees or groups suckered from one tree are self-sterile.

- Pick berries in July/August, just before the birds get them. In good years, cherry stones can be gathered from beneath the tree in August.

- Store unripe fruit in plastic bags until soft or partly rotten, and then wash to remove the pulp. Ripe flesh can be easily removed.

- Sow immediately in pots, trays or outdoor beds, protected from mice and birds.

- OR store in a sealed container in a cool place until October. Then stratify outdoors for 4 months, before sowing in spring.

- OR store in a sealed container in a cool place until October. Then mix with a medium and keep warm for 2 weeks, and then chill for 18 weeks, before sowing in spring.

Cherry, bird (*Prunus padus*)

- Note locations of trees when in flower in May, as the tree is not conspicuous at other times of year. Produces small, bitter black fruits which ripen in July.

- Propagate as for wild cherry.

Crab apple (*Malus sylvestris*)

- Good seed crops every 1-2 years.

- Pick fruits in October.

- Extract seed immediately and stratify outdoors until February.

- OR warm for 2 weeks, and then chill for 14 weeks.

- OR store fruit in a cool place until January and then cut open to extract seed and sow immediately.

- Sow in pots, trays or outdoor beds. Lightly cover seed with sand or compost.

Elm, English (*Ulmus procera*)

- Seeds are sterile. Propagate from suckers.

Elm, wych (*Ulmus glabra*)

- Good seed crops every 1-2 years.

- Collect seeds in May/early June.

- Sow immediately in pots, trays or outdoor beds, lightly covered with compost and kept moist. Germination is very quick, and seedlings should make significant growth in the first year.

Holly (*Ilex aquifolium*)

- Good seed crops every 2-3 years.

- Collect berries between November and February.

- Stratify outdoors for 16 months.

- OR mix with medium and store in warmth for 40 weeks then chill for 24 weeks before sowing.

- Sow in pots, or in trays for pricking out into pots. Holly resents root disturbance – avoid transplanting after the first year.

Hornbeam (*Carpinus betulus*)

- Good seed crops every 2-4 years.

- Collect in November, while wing is still slightly green, for immediate sowing.

- OR collect from November-spring, when wing is brown and seed coat is hard. Seed can then be stored as necessary.

- To break dormancy, stratify outdoors for 18 months, protected from mice and birds.

- OR mix with medium and store in warmth for 4 weeks, then chill for 12-24 weeks.

- Sow in pots, trays or outdoor seedbeds.

Lime, small-leaved (*Tilia cordata*)

- Good seed crops every 2-3 years.

- Collect seeds in October.

- Stratify outdoors for 18 months.

- OR mix with medium, and store in warmth for 4-8 weeks, and then chill for 16 weeks.

- Sow in pots, trays or outdoor beds.

Lime, large-leaved (*Tilia platyphyllos*)

- Propagate as for small-leaved lime.

Maple, field (*Acer campestre*)

- Good seed crops every year.

- Collect the winged seeds in September/ October, when they are still a yellow to light brown colour, before they form a hard seed coat.

- Sow seed immediately.

- OR mix with medium and store in warmth for 4-8 weeks, then chill for 12-24 weeks.

- Sow in pots, trays or outdoor beds.

Oak, pedunculate (*Quercus robur*)

- Good seed crops every 2-4 years.

- Collect from September to November. The first acorns to fall are usually infertile. Normally the morning after the first frost there will be a large fall of acorns.

- Preferably sow straight away in pots, trays or outdoor seedbeds, as stored seed loses viability. Protect from predators with extra layer of soil (p52) or netting (p53).

- OR store in hessian bags hung up in a cool place. Shake gently every few days to prevent the acorns heating up. Gently spray with cool water at intervals from January until sowing time, to prevent the acorns shrivelling and to keep them plump and viable.

- Sow in pots or outdoor beds.

Oak, sessile (*Quercus petraea*)

- As for pedunculate oak.

Rowan (*Sorbus aucuparia*)

- Good seed crops every 2-3 years.

- Collect fully ripe seed, macerate and sow immediately, for germination the following March.

Service tree (*Sorbus torminalis*)

- Seeds most years.

- Pick berries in September, when brown and ripe.

- Store in poly bags until partly rotten.

- Wash to remove pulp and sow immediately in pots, trays or outdoor beds.

- OR stratify cleaned seeds outdoors, and sow in late winter.

Scots pine (*Pinus sylvestris*)

- Good seed crops every 2-3 years.

- Collect cones from November to February, before they open. Dry in a warm room until they open and the seeds drop out.

- Store seed in a sealed container in the fridge.

- Four weeks before you wish to sow, mix the seeds with a medium and return to the fridge to chill.

- OR use 'shallow dormancy' method (p44).

- Sow in pots, trays or outdoor beds, covering the seeds lightly. Keep moist.

Sweet chestnut (*Castanea sativa*)

- Seeds every 1-4 years, with best seed after a warm summer.

- Gather fallen nuts from the ground or pick from the trees as soon as the outer cases begin to break open, in October/ November.

- Sow immediately in free-draining soils, protected from birds and animals.

- OR spread the nuts out to surface dry for about a week in a protected, shaded, ventilated place, then store in hessian sacks, hung up in a cool, dry place. Spray weekly to keep moist. Sow in spring.

Whitebeam (*Sorbus aria*)

- As for rowan.

Yew (*Taxus baccata*)

- Crops most years.

- Collect from September to November. The seed and red flesh are poisonous.

- Soak to remove flesh.

- Stratify outdoors for 16 months.

- OR mix with medium, keep in warmth for 40 weeks, then chill for 20-24 weeks.

- Sow in pots, trays or outdoor beds.

SHRUBS

Blackthorn (*Prunus spinosa*)

- Seeds every 1-2 years.
- Pick when fruit is blue-black, in October.
- Soak to extract seed from pulp.
- Keep in warmth for 2 weeks, then chill for 18 weeks.
- Sow in trays or outdoor beds.

Broom (*Cytisus scoparius*)

- Seeds every year.
- Pick pods when black, in August.
- Pop pods to extract seeds.
- Store seed in a sealed container until spring.
- Sow in pots, as plants resent root disturbance.

Buckthorn, alder (*Frangula alnus*)

- Propagate as for purging buckthorn.
- Keep seedlings and young plants moist.

Buckthorn, purging (*Rhamnus catharticus*)

- Seeds most years, on female plants in mixed groups.
- Gather fruits when fully black in autumn.
- Stratify outdoors.
- OR store and then chill for 8 weeks.
- Sow in February, in pots, trays or outdoor beds.

Dogwood (*Cornus sanguinea*)

- Seeds every year.
- Pick berries as soon as they change from green to black in late summer, before birds get them. Sow immediately.
- OR soak to soften flesh.
- Then stratify outdoors until spring.
- OR warm for 10 weeks and then chill for 10 weeks.
- Sow in pots, trays or outdoor beds.
- Can also be propagated from cuttings, suckers or layers.

Elder (*Sambucus nigra*)

- Gather ripe berries and keep in poly bags until partly rotten, or crush in a blender, and then wash out the seeds.
- Stratify outdoors.
- Sow in pots, trays or outdoor beds in late winter.
- OR propagate from hardwood cuttings taken with a heel in October/November.

Gorse (*Ulex europaeus*)

- As for broom.

Guelder rose (*Viburnum opulus*)

- Good seed crops most years.
- Gather fruits in August/September before they are fully ripe.
- Store fruit in poly bags until partly rotten.
- Separate seed from flesh by washing. Sow immediately.
- OR keep in warmth for 8 weeks, and then chill for 8 weeks. Even after this treatment, germination may be erratic.
- Sow in trays or beds and cover with 2cm (1") of soil.

Hawthorn (*Crataegus monogyna*)

- Good seed crops every 1-2 years.
- Collect haws in September/October, when fully ripe.
- Soak to remove pulp from seeds.
- Stratify outdoors for 18 months.
- OR mix with medium and store in warmth for 4-8 weeks, then chill for 12-16 weeks.
- Sow in pots, trays or outdoor beds.

Hazel (*Corylus avellana*)

- Good seed crops every 2-3 years.
- First nuts that fall are usually sterile. Pick from the tree in August/September just as nuts begin to turn brown. Fully ripe nuts will fall to the ground, but they must be gathered promptly as birds or squirrels will take them.
- Place nuts in water and discard sterile ones which float to the surface.
- Sow immediately in pots or trays.
- OR stratify outdoors for 6 months.

- OR store for up to 4 weeks in a hessian bag hung up in a cool, airy place and then chill for 16 weeks before sowing.
- When sowing in pots or trays, use a dibber or similar to make a hole so that the top of the nut is just covered. For outdoor beds, broadcast the nuts and then cover with a layer of soil or compost. Protect from mice and birds.

Juniper (*Juniperus communis*)

- Propagate from cuttings, taken with a heel in late summer from that season's growth.
- OR gather berries in October.
- Seeds have 'double dormancy' (both hard coat and embryo) and require either 18 months' stratification or accelerated cold-warm-cold treatment.

Spindle (*Euonymus europaeus*)

- Seeds most years.
- Collect in September. Remove bright pink cases which enclose the orange seeds. Note that all parts of the seed are toxic.
- Dry in a warm room until seed covering can be removed by beating the seeds in a bag.
- Store in warmth for 10 weeks and then chill for 12 weeks.
- Sow in pots, trays or outdoor seedbeds, covered with a thin layer of coarse sand.
- Germination is erratic, so leave until at least the second spring.

Wayfaring tree (*Viburnum lantana*)

- Seeds most years.
- Gather in August as soon as at least a few berries in each cluster turn from red to black.
- Macerate until flesh can be removed.
- Sow immediately.
- OR stratify outdoors until spring.
- OR store in warmth for 8 weeks and then chill for 8 weeks.
- Sow into pots or trays and germinate in a greenhouse or cold frame.

THE BEST WAY TO PLANT

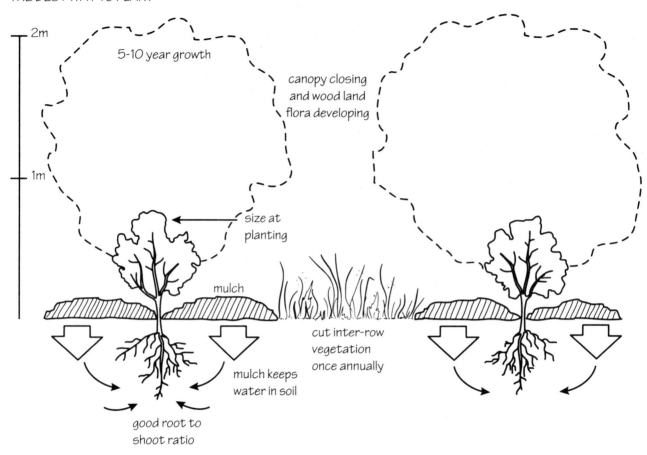

2m

5-10 year growth

canopy closing
and wood land
flora developing

1m

size at
planting

mulch

cut inter-row
vegetation
once annually

mulch keeps
water in soil

good root to
shoot ratio

THE WORST WAY TO PLANT

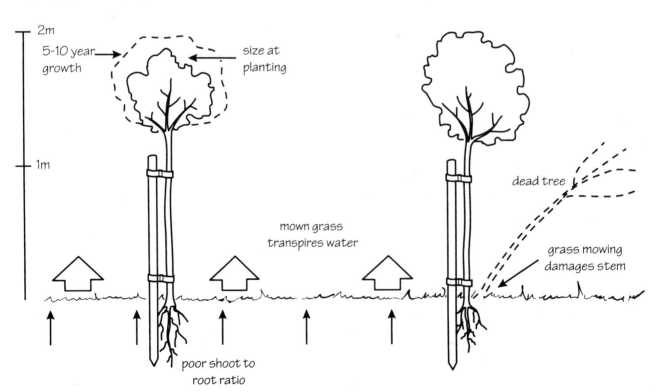

2m

5-10 year
growth

size at
planting

1m

dead tree

mown grass
transpires water

grass mowing
damages stem

poor shoot to
root ratio

6   Planting and protection

This chapter describes the practical techniques for planting trees. The use of treeshelters and other products for enhancing and protecting growth is described. Weed control, which is the most important part of tree care in the years after planting, is detailed in chapter 7.

Preparation for planting

SIZE OF TREES TO PLANT

Always buy small, young trees. These establish much more quickly than bigger, older trees of the same species, which they will soon catch up and overtake in size. The reason is that good quality young plants have a mass of fibrous roots but only a short, sturdy stem. They establish quickly without any check to growth. Larger bare-root trees have a much poorer root:shoot ratio, with a small root system for the amount of top growth. The root system often gets damaged during lifting, transport or planting, with few of the vital fibrous roots and root hairs remaining intact. Large trees therefore establish much more slowly, often putting on little or no growth for several years after planting, by which time younger plants will have caught up. Bigger, older plants require longer care in the nursery, so they are also more expensive to buy, or require longer voluntary hours of care in a tree nursery. Large trees are more difficult to transport to the planting site, and take longer to plant. Because of the effort involved in digging large holes, they are more likely to be planted badly.

Bigger trees, such as 'standard' trees, also need staking at planting time to stop them being blown over by the wind. If tall stakes are used, these stop the natural movement of the tree in the wind, which stimulates it to thicken at the base of the trunk, and to grow roots that buttress against the wind. When the stake is eventually removed, the tree may be unstable. Stakes and ties are expensive, and need annual checking. When people think that planting a standard tree is a short-cut to growing a mature tree or an 'instant' woodland, they must be persuaded otherwise! Even for planting specimen trees, or for a 'ceremonial' planting, it's much better to plant small, even if it does look rather insignificant on the planting day. For single or specimen trees, it's better to spend less on the tree, and more on the tree surround or other protection.

Small transplants are usually less prone to vandalism than older trees, because they are less noticeable, and less inviting as a target. If small transplants do get damaged, they can be cut back to ground level to sprout again, with only the loss of a year's growth.

About the only exception to this rule is when planting fruit trees or some ornamental trees, which may only be available as standards.

Seedlings, undercuts and transplants are young trees which are up to 1.2m tall and up to three or four years old, as listed below. Note the following:

- 'Seedlings' are plants which until lifting, were not moved from the place where they were sown.

- 'Undercuts' have not been moved, but have been undercut by a spade or special implement to encourage bushy roots. For example, 1 u 1 describes a plant which has been grown from seed for a year, then undercut, and then grown for another year.

- 'Transplants' have been transplanted in the nursery, to encourage good root development. For example, 1 + 2 describes a plant which has been grown from seed for a year, transplanted, and then grown on for two years.

- Cell-grown plants are seedlings grown in small containers of compost, called cells, of which 'Rootrainers' are the best known product. They are planted out with the rootball or 'plug' intact. Various sizes of cell are available (p47) to suit different species. Plants may be despatched still in their cells, or removed and with the plugs wrapped in clingfilm or similar. They may be referred to as, for example, C1 (cell-grown for one year) or P1 (one year old plug).

For most conservation planting, choose from the range of nursery stock sizes given overleaf in Table 6a.

Note the following:

- For most woodland creation and restocking projects, young transplants (1 + 1) are the best choice, as they are cheap and establish quickly. For any given species, the price of plants relates to the number of years spent in the nursery.

- For quick establishment after planting, bare-root stock should have a fibrous, bushy root system, and a sturdy stem. Although height is used to grade bare-root plants, the thickness of the root collar is a better guide. For example, a 30cm tall transplant should have a root collar diameter of at least 5mm. A transplant (eg 1 +1), which is the same height as a seedling (1 + 0) of the same

Table 6a: Nursery stock sizes for forestry, conservation and amenity planting

BARE-ROOT STOCK	HEIGHT RANGE (cm)
Seedling (1 + 0)	15-30
Undercut (.5+.5, 1 u 1, etc)	30-90
Transplant (1+1, 1+2, etc)	20-120

CELL-GROWN STOCK	HEIGHT RANGE (cm)
Seedling (1 + 0), 'Rootrainer'	15-60

Table 6b: Nursery stock sizes for ornamental planting

NAME	Circumference of stem 1m above ground (cm)	Min height (m)	Max height (m)	Clear stem height to lowest branch (m)
Whip	-	1.2	2.5	-
Feathered whip	-	1.8	3.0	-
Half-standard	-	1.8	2.1	1.2 - 1.5
Standard	8-10	2.75	3.0	1.8 (min)

species, should have a thicker root collar, a better root system and will normally establish more successfully.

• Rootrainers are more expensive than similar size bare-root seedlings, but have various advantages (p72).

Nursery stock older than about three years are categorised as given above. These tend to be high value ornamental and introduced species, for planting in parks and gardens. They are much more expensive than seedlings, undercuts and transplants, and are much slower to establish. They may be available bare-root, root-balled, container-grown or containerised. Root-balled stock is grown in the open ground, lifted and wrapped for planting. Containerised plants have been grown in open ground and then put into containers.

SOIL PREPARATION

In general it is much better to work with the existing soil conditions by choice of tree species and planting design, rather than by trying to change the soil conditions. Tree species that naturally suit the site will establish easily and grow quickly (p21). The best guide to species that suit the soil is to look at what's growing nearby. On highly disturbed soils or industrial sites, test pits may need to be dug at various points over the planting site at an early stage in planning the project, in order to assess the soil type.

Even for a commercial woodland, 20% of open, unplanted area within the wood is considered acceptable (p22), so it is not a good idea to plant every part of the planned woodland area. Waterlogged or seasonally wet ground is likely to anyway be a valuable habitat as it is, and may be best left unplanted.

Trees can grow in most parts of Britain below about 600m (2,000ft), and they do not need fertile topsoil to grow. As shown by a glance at any abandoned railway siding, birch, willow and other pioneer species will establish in apparently poor conditions. The roots of seedling trees are strong growing, and can make their way down through dry stones to find water and nutrients. However, sufficient depth of soil is necessary for secure root anchorage (see opposite).

seedling birch growing on railway siding

Fertile ground is more difficult than poor ground for tree establishment, because weeds compete much more strongly. Trees will ultimately reach a greater size on fertile, well-watered land, but in the early years will require more management than on poorer soils.

Clay soils

Clay soils can be a problem. They do not drain well, and become waterlogged in winter. This makes planting difficult, and the lack of air within the soil can kill the plant roots. Planting in individual pits (p79) and back-filling with compost is not a good idea, as the pit will fill with water. Planting on mounds or ridges does not alleviate the problem, as this merely worsens problems in summer.

In summer clay soils can dry out and even crack, so young trees suffer from drought. Planting notches may open up, exposing tree roots to the air. Pit planting but backfilling with the same soil may be the best method, finished with a generous mulch of compost spread around the tree to reduce drying of the soil surface (p100).

On large sites, clay soils can be improved by deep cultivation using agricultural machinery, as detailed below for compacted soils. On small sites, you will need to rely on careful choice of species, together with mulching and weed control so that lack of water in summer is not a problem. Avoid planting in the wettest areas.

Drying of clay soils can vary over a site according to the vegetation cover. Weed free strips or areas of ground kept clear by herbicide, to benefit tree growth, tend to crack worse than adjacent grass-covered ground.

Compacted soil

This is soil which has been spoiled by heavy machinery or other use. Heavy use squashes and damages the soil, spoiling its structure. The movement of water and air through the soil is impeded, and roots and other organisms find it difficult to penetrate the ground. The soil becomes waterlogged in winter, rock hard in summer, and 'lifeless'. A normal healthy soil contains a large proportion of air space, with easy movement of organisms, minerals and water within the soil, making a good environment for tree roots to grow.

Persistent use of heavy machinery, for example on industrial land, can cause soil compaction quite deep down into the soil. Car-parking, sports or even a single use by crowds of people in wet conditions can compact the surface layer. Repeated ploughing to the same depth can create a compacted layer, called a plough pan, on arable land. Soil that has been moved by machinery, especially if moved in wet conditions, is often compacted. Sometimes compaction is done deliberately, for example on embankments, to reduce the movement of water through the soil, thereby increasing stability.

Deeply compacted soils can be loosened by 'ripping'. This requires a crawler-tractor with deep tines, or heavy-duty agricultural subsoilers that rip the soil down to a depth of 50cm (1.5') or more, shattering the hardened ground. This operation must be done in dry weather, or it will simply cause further damage. Where ripping is necessary, it must be done in the summer before planting.

Surface compaction can be alleviated by normal ploughing, which needs to be done in dry conditions. Plough pans can be broken up with an agricultural subsoiler.

Thin soils

Although trees can establish on stony soils, as they get bigger they need a sufficient rooting depth to give secure anchorage. Mature trees of most species need at least a 1m (3') depth of soil or rootable soil material to give secure anchorage. In natural conditions, shallow or stony soils are usually in exposed or upland situations, where the wind, altitude and other factors stunt the tree's growth, so that root anchorage is sufficient for the size of tree. A tree grown in very shallow soil in a sheltered, lowland situation may grow to a reasonable size, but then be wind-blown due to lack of rooting depth. On thin soils, choose pioneer species and 'scrub' species such as birch, sallow, blackthorn and others which are either fairly short-lived or of low ultimate height. Alders and poplars may also be suitable. Leguminous species such as gorse and broom, or the introduced laburnum, robinia or other species may be a way of establishing woody cover on very poor soils.

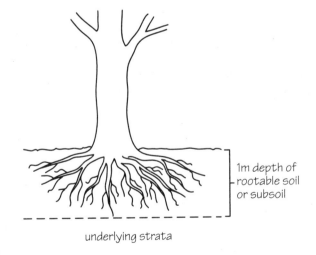

1m depth of rootable soil or subsoil

underlying strata

Contaminated land

Some soils will not support tree growth due to various forms of contamination from industrial activity. This can include extremes of pH, the presence of toxic materials, excess rubble and stone or contamination from organic materials. There may be physical barriers to rooting, such as concrete below the soil surface. Soils which are bare of vegetation are very likely to be a problem. Get advice from the Forestry Commission before planning planting on disused industrial land. Advice should be sought from the

Environment Agency before any work is undertaken on land that may be contaminated. The Agency keep a register of contaminated land, as advised by local authorities.

Some old industrial sites support an interesting ground flora and associated fauna that has developed due to the limitations of the site, which prevent its progression through to woodland. Your site assessment (p9) should highlight any such areas, which should be left as they are. Limited tree or hedge planting could be carried out for screening purposes, in any pockets of suitable soil.

Soil ameliorants

When planting bare-root stock, it is not normally advisable to backfill the planting pit with organic material such as garden compost or peat. As well as the extra expense, there may be adverse effects, as listed below.

- In clay soils, the organic matter increases the amount of water retention in a pit which may already be prone to waterlogging, leading to anaerobic conditions which kill plant roots.

- The interface where the backfill and the surrounding soil meet can open up in dry weather, damaging the roots.

- Micro-organisms acting on peat absorb nitrogen, which may lead to soil in the planting pit becoming nitrogen deficient.

However, there may be benefit in adding organic matter from an existing woodland floor, which can contain mycorrhiza to aid tree establishment and growth (see below). A gritty material, for example half coarse grit and half compost, mixed into the backfill at planting may improve root growth in heavy clay soils.

Water-storing granules (p57) can be added at planting. They can absorb hundreds of times their own weight in water, which is then available to the plant as needed through dry periods. The granules also help nutrient availability and aerate heavy or compacted soils. Granules are worth using in poor soils, where they will help reduce plant losses in the first year or two after planting. Normal weed control measures (p97) must also be used, or the benefit of the granules will be lost.

Inorganic fertilisers should not normally be added when planting bare-root stock. The fine roots which are able to absorb fertiliser are mainly lost during transplanting, and regenerate during the first growing season after planting. By the time they have regrown, inorganic fertilisers will either have leached away, or worse, have been absorbed by weed growth, causing further stress to the young tree. Even if fertilisers do promote shoot growth in the first growing season, this is not an advantage, as it worsens the imbalance in the root:shoot ratio which has already been caused by transplanting.

Mycorrhiza

Mycorrhiza result from the symbiosis between certain soil fungi and the roots of plants, including those of trees, shrubs, grasses and herbaceous perennials. The fungus receives sugar and plant hormones from the plant, and the plant is supplied with water and dissolved nutrients from the fungus. The plants and the fungi become inseparably linked, with each becoming totally dependent on the other. Mycorrhiza are very common and vital to woodlands and other ecosystems, with many different types that each have a specific role to play.

For many plants the nutrient and water uptake is mainly by way of the mycorrhiza, and not directly through the roots. It's estimated that the fungal network extends the volume of soils that plant roots can exploit for water and soil nutrients by a factor of 12 to 15. The mycorrhizal threads are more efficient than plant roots at nutrient uptake, being finer and more active. Mycorrhizal associations also promote root branching, so helping to form a better root system.

Mycorrhiza are probably the main reason for the marked difference in growth between naturally occurring seedling trees, and transplanted trees. Natural seedlings usually occur in ground which already supports the appropriate type of mycorrhizal growth, so the symbiotic relationship is established early on and the young trees grow well. Cultivated soils, reclaimed industrial land and other disturbed and non-wooded sites have little or no mycorrhizal activity.

The significance of mycorrhiza in establishing trees and shrubs on difficult sites has only recently been realised.

Mycorrhizal activity can be encouraged by the following techniques. It's interesting to note how understanding of mycorrhizal activity gives a scientific base to the natural 'organic' methods of cultivation that many people have developed in the past through instinct or experience. Permaculture also follows similar principles.

- Minimise soil cultivation and disturbance to avoid damaging the mycelial network.

- Avoid creating bare ground, as it will become colonised by ruderal or weed species that are typically non-mycorrhizal.

- Where sites are being disturbed, save any topsoil and store it carefully. If it's to be left for some time, sow it with native grasses and herbs which may encourage mycorrhizal growth.

- Avoid single-species planting, as this will limit the range of mycorrhiza which develop.

- If fertiliser has to be used on nutrient poor sites, only use slow-release fertiliser.

- Incorporate leaf litter and natural composts (see below).

- Avoid water run-off as this can wash away mycorrhizal spores.

- Control weeds. As well as the other disadvantages to tree growth, it's thought that some weed species may inhibit the development of mycorrhiza.

Mycorrhizal activity can be encouraged by inoculation with a commercial product, which can be introduced to plants in the nursery, or applied at planting. Various products are available, including root dips, powders and liquids. MycorTree Root Dip (Plant Health Care), for example, is used on bare-root stock before potting on or planting out. The dip contains live spores of beneficial mycorrhizal fungi, hydrogel to enhance drought tolerance, and various biocatalysts. The product is mixed with water in a bucket, into which the tree roots are dipped so that they are coated with gel. Plant or pot on immediately after dipping. The MycoForce range of products (Symbio) include dips, powders, tablets and other products for nursery stock and for use at planting.

The ground around existing trees which are under stress can also be inoculated. This has recently been done to many mature trees at Kew gardens, resulting in improvements in canopy cover from 45% up to 95% in less than a year (*Horticulture Week*, 4 March,1999).

For do-it-yourself techniques, the best way is to introduce some organic material from existing woods. You must get permission from the landowner before you remove any material. Select a site underneath the canopy of the species of tree which you are planting. Rake away the top 25cm (1") layer of leaf litter from an area of about two square metres (2 sq yards), and then carefully scrape away the top centimetre (half inch) or so of organic material, and shovel it into a sack. Take great care not to damage any surface roots. Then rake the leaves back over the scraped area. Collect the material as near as possible to planting time, to avoid it deteriorating in storage. When planting, add about half a spade of the organic material to the planting hole or notch.

Leaf mould has long been used by gardeners as a mulch and compost. Many councils recycle their leaf sweepings and other plant material by making the resulting compost available within their area. Gather your own leaf mould by raking up leaves from lawns and hard surfaces, and store in heaps or bottomless bins, preferably sited on a woodland soil where any existing mycorrhiza can spread into the compost. Alternatively, try inoculating the heap with some organic material from an existing wood. The leaf mould should be stored for at least a year before it is used. Rotate the use of the heaps, so that you use the oldest material first.

EXISTING VEGETATION

In general, when planting into a grass sward such as a pasture or mown grass, it's much better to plant direct into the sward, and then use herbicide or mulch after planting to kill the grass. If you try and remove the turf by digging, ploughing or herbicide, in order to start in 'clean ground', you are much more likely to have problems with weeds. An invasion of docks, nettles, thistles, couch grass and other weeds will be more troublesome than the grass sward.

Scrub and bramble are valuable wildlife habitats as they are. On sites where poor soil or exposure to the wind are limitations, bramble with small trees such as blackthorn and hawthorn are likely to be the 'climax vegetation', and planting other species of trees is not appropriate. However, on some fertile sites, such as abandoned farmland or allotments, bramble and scrub can take hold, and it may be the desired aim to accelerate the process to woodland. Bramble and scrub are impossible to eradicate simply by cutting down, and will quickly regrow. Depending on the aims of the planting, the best technique for establishing trees is to make use of the shelter and protection afforded by the scrub, by planting pockets within it.

Clear areas of at least 5m (16') square and plant groups of about five trees within the cleared area. Protect as necessary against animal damage. Marker poles or a detailed plan are useful so that pockets don't get forgotten during maintenance. You will need to return frequently, probably twice during each growing season, to cut back encroaching bramble and scrub. Once the leading shoots of the new trees are clear of the scrub there should be no further need to weed. As the canopy of the new trees closes over, the growth of scrub will be suppressed.

The restocking of woodland or replanting of areas within existing woodland is not covered in detail in this handbook. Often however the same considerations as above apply, as gaps within a canopy which are large enough to support new trees also encourage the growth of bramble and other scrub species. Try and look at the proposed planting area in summer. What appears to be a large gap in a wood in winter will appear very much smaller when the woodland is in full leaf. Generally soils in woodland should be good for tree growth, but localised compaction may have occurred during extraction of timber from the woodland. See Broad (1998) for details of restocking existing woodlands.

PLANTING SEASON

Planting time must be co-ordinated with the time the trees are available from the nursery, which, for bare-root trees, will depend on the date that the top growth becomes dormant in autumn (p58). Over most of lowland Britain, the optimum is that plants are lifted from the nursery and planted out in their final positions as soon as possible after this date. This allows planting while the soil is still warm and not too wet, making planting operations easier and less damaging to the soil structure. Root growth can continue while the soil remains warm (>6°C), even though top growth is dormant, and there is a burst of root growth just before bud burst in spring. In spring, the plants will get away to the best possible start, with roots well established before any drought sets in.

Most nurseries aim to have stock available for planting from about October to March, and may use various treatments in order to induce dormancy (p58), or cold storage to delay bud burst. The onset of dormancy occurs later on nurseries in the south and west, on mild sites or during mild autumns, and current climatic trends are for winters to start later and end earlier.

In the mild parts of the south and west, planting may not be able to start until late November if locally produced stock is used, as the onset of dormancy will be late. Alternatively, stock from northern nurseries, which normally becomes dormant at least 2 weeks earlier, may be obtained for earlier planting. In mild winters in the south and west, planting is possible from December to February.

In colder areas, planting should only commence when soil temperatures begin to increase in February or March. There may be high losses of stock planted earlier due to deterioration during the delay before root growth commences. Plant exposed, high elevation sites from mid-March onwards. Stock which is cold stored, in order to delay bud burst, can be used from early April until mid-May.

For recommended dates for lifting and planting of broadleaves, see the table on page 59.

Plants lifted from the nursery should be planted in their final positions with the minimum of delay. Nurseries should lift to order, and deliver as quickly as possible, although plants can be stored in bags for short periods (p59).

Evergreens including holly, yew or juniper are best planted in either the autumn or spring, when the roots are active. Avoid the coldest period of the winter. These species are container-grown, making the planting date less crucial than for bare-root plants. Scots pine and other conifers are normally planted bare-root.

Cell-grown or container-grown plants can theoretically be planted at any time of year. However, autumn planting should be the rule for all but the coldest sites, for the reasons given above. The great advantage of cell-grown trees for growers and planters is that an earlier start to the planting season can be made, so spreading the workload over a longer period. September is the best time to plant. Moving a cell-grown plant mid-way through the growing season from the shelter of the nursery to an open planting site is

likely to be damaging, and watering will be required until the plants are established.

Weather

If there is a choice, plant on dull, drizzly days, rather than in windy, sunny weather. The fine root hairs are damaged by even a short exposure to drying winds, and such damage will be minimised if the conditions are damp. Cell-grown plants will also suffer less stress if planted in moist, dull weather.

PRE-PLANTING CARE

The trees should be supplied from the nursery in special sealed plastic sacks, which are white on the outside and black on the inside, to prevent the roots from drying or warming. If the trees can't be planted straight away, they can be stored as they are in a cool, dark building for two to three weeks.

The plastic sacks must be handled very carefully, and should not be thrown down, trampled on or stacked up, as the plants inside will get damaged. Store the sacks upright and loosely packed. Do not open them, or the plants will dry out.

If there is no suitable cool indoor storage, the plants will have to be taken out of the sacks and placed in a shallow trench with roots covering the soil. If the plants are tied in bundles, don't undo them at this stage. Use fine soil to cover the roots, so it trickles down between the roots and protects them. If the weather is dry, water the covered trench to keep the soil moist. Make sure that no-one walks on the trench, as the roots are only just below the surface and will be damaged by trampling.

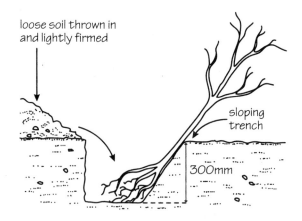

loose soil thrown in and lightly firmed

sloping trench

300mm

Any handling of plants between delivery and planting should be minimised, because even a few moments' exposure to the air damages the fine roots. Transfer of bare-root plants from sack to trench, from trench to planting bag or during final planting must be done speedily but carefully.

WORK RATES AND ORGANISATION

Work rates

Rates vary greatly, depending on the terrain, and the experience and organisation of the planters. Rates for experienced volunteers are about 80-100 notch-planted transplants per person per day, or 50-75 if fitted with tree shelters. Pit planting takes longer, with about 20-30 whips per person per day a reasonable average. School children or inexperienced volunteers will be considerably slower.

- It's usually easier to work in pairs. One person measures the spacing, cuts the notch and holds it open with the spade, while the other person quickly transfers the plant from the planting bag to the notch.

- Separate teams can check the trees are firm, and fit tree shelters, guards and mulches.

- Others can keep the teams supplied with trees and other materials.

- Swap the teams around from time to time.

- At the end of the day, make sure all unplanted trees are sealed in bags, and that all unused trees and materials are removed from the site.

Careful thought and planning needs to be given to the organisation of the planting operation. The method used will depend on the size of the planting project and the numbers of people involved. General guidelines are given below for large and small projects.

Organisation of large projects

This could include projects of about half a hectare (an acre) or more, involving the planting of 1000 trees or more, over several planting days.

The planting plan will contain the details of the planting areas, the species to be planted and the spacing. As explained in chapter 2, a simple plan which relates strongly to the site, and which has a limited number of species will be easier to plant and ultimately more successful than something which is unnecessarily complicated.

The information contained in the planting plan needs to be marked on the site in a simple way which the planters can follow. The plan will show the total area to be planted, with paths, glades, damp areas and other open spaces to be left unplanted. For some schemes, the planting area may be divided into plots or 'compartments', each characterised by a particular mixture of species or method of management. For each plot, the plan will show the total number of each species to be planted, and the spacing between them.

In advance of planting, each plot needs to be clearly marked on the ground. Plots should have been designed to relate strongly to the physical features of the site, so some boundaries will be obvious, such as streams or changes of slope. Hedges, walls and other man-made boundaries will also partly delineate plots. Elsewhere, mark the edges of each plot with canes, road pins and tape (as used in roadworks) or similar. Where these might be vandalised, spray paint, dye used in herbicide application (p119) or a line of sand can be used.

For each plot, make sure you have the correct number of trees of each species ready. Bare-root stock in bags should be labelled with the plot name or number, and the species name. If you have to split bags or bundles of trees between plots, do it quickly to minimise root drying, and reseal the bags. Rootrainers or similar which are no longer in their plastic cells should also be protected in bags, and labelled. It's best to do any sorting before the planters arrive in order to avoid any delay when plants may be exposed to drying. It's easier if the plan has been drawn up with round numbers of species for each plot, to avoid having to split bags between plots (p60).

Spacing will normally be uniform throughout the plot. There are various methods of marking the spacing:

- One or two people can work ahead of the planters, marking the planting lines with three or more canes for each line. The planters then sight along the canes to find the line, and use a cane or similar to measure the lateral spacing.

- Alternatively, each planter works individually over part of the plot, using a measured cane to locate each planting position, in a triangular pattern.

LINE PLANTING

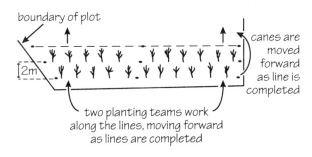

two planting teams work along the lines, moving forward as lines are completed

TRIANGULAR PLANTING

two planting teams work separately

- An alternative way of marking line planting when working on one's own is shown below.

LINE PLANTING
one person working on own

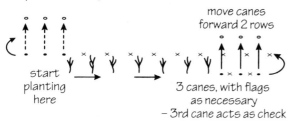

start planting here

move canes forward 2 rows

3 canes, with flags as necessary – 3rd cane acts as check

Planting lines make it easier to keep to patterns of groups of nine of each species, for example. It's also easier to maintain the supply of plants, stakes, shelters and so on to the planters. Avoid having people walking through the newly planted area, apart from those who are fitting guards or mulch mats.

Either of these methods have sufficient room for error that the overall result will be informal, rather than strict rows of trees. Discrepancies from the pattern will also occur due to irregularities in the ground. Any very damp areas, not noted on the plan, should be left unplanted.

On most large scale schemes, species are planted in groups of 9 to 40, according to the overall scale of the planting and then thinned. An example might be 60% oak, 20% birch, 20% rowan, to be planted in groups of 9 across the plot. The groups are usually selected randomly, rather than following a set pattern, in order to create a more natural effect in the field. This random pattern can be worked out on a plan, but following a plan is usually unworkable for plots of more than about 50 plants, as very accurate field measurements are needed both to draw up the plan, and to attempt to follow it.

It's better to implement 'randomness' in the field by using the 'coloured bead' technique, or similar. For the above example, you could have six orange (oak), two blue (birch)

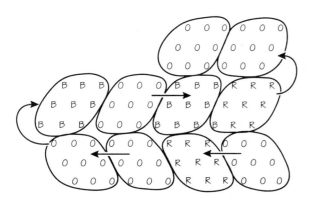

O = Oak   60%
B = Birch   20%
R = Rowan   20% in groups of 9

and two red (rowan) beads, counters, lego bricks or similar in your pocket. At each position for a group of plants, you transfer a bead from one pocket to another, and plant the corresponding species. Mathematically this works best if you work up one line and down the next, without coming up against another team working randomly!

In practice things will not work out this neatly. Discrepancies will occur at the ends of lines, at irregularities in the ground, and where planting teams meet. As long as the lines and spacings are followed, so that at the end of the day all the trees are planted to fill the designated area, the exact pattern of groups will not matter. The main thing is to get all the trees planted properly and quickly.

At events where people are encouraged to bring their own special tree for planting, you need to plan carefully, as participants will not be pleased to find out their special tree is likely to be removed during thinning!

Organisation of small projects

Typical projects are school or community planting schemes, involving the planting of perhaps 200 or 300 trees. Normally planting would be done in one day.

Before the planters arrive, someone familiar with the scheme should mark the position of each tree or group of trees with a cane, following the plan. The canes should be colour coded with tape or similar to indicate which species is to be planted. On sites secure from vandalism this can be done on an earlier day. The trees, still securely wrapped in bags if bare-root stock, should be neatly laid out at one or more points at the edge of the site. Each bag should be clearly marked with the species name or colour code.

Where planting is being done during a school day, the children should be organised to come out onto the planting site in groups at intervals during the day. For each group, explain the purpose of the planting and show them how to plant a tree. A pair of children then each plants one or more trees. Concentrate on one part of the site at a time, and avoid having the children walk, or worse run, through the part of the site which is already planted. For bare-root stock, each pair of children should have a plastic carrier bag in which to protect the roots of their tree while they carry it from the 'supply' point to the planting site. At all costs avoid having the children walk around carrying unprotected bare-root trees. In the time taken to carry the plant, choose the cane, dig the notch and so on, the tree roots will have been damaged by exposure to the air. Alternatively, other people can carry the plants in the bags to the planting position, and only take the tree out when the notch or hole is ready.

For secondary school children, each team can then fit the treeshelter, guard or mulch mat as necessary. With younger children, it's usually best if more experienced volunteers follow up with this work later in the day, or on another day.

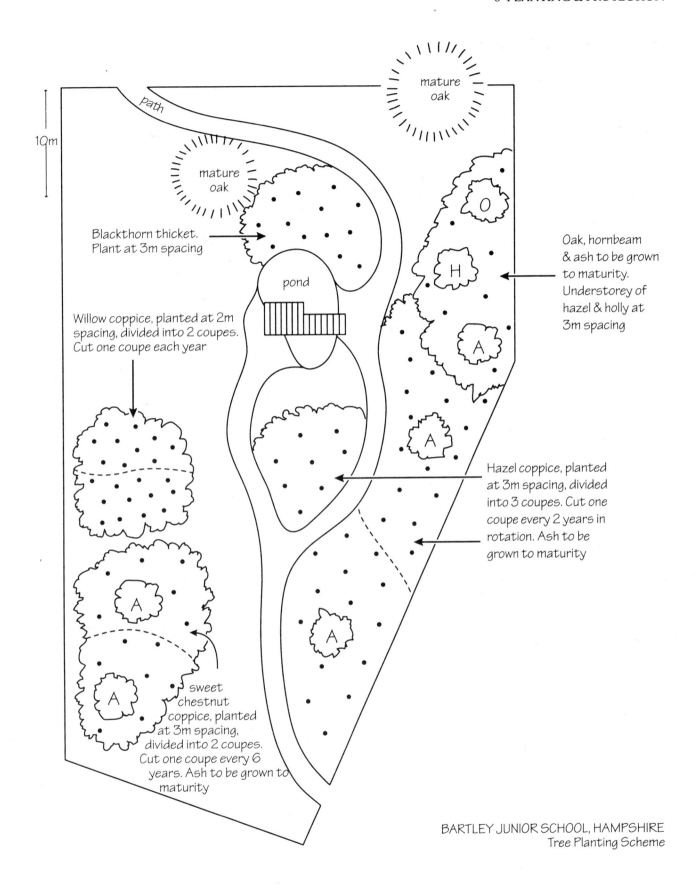

Blackthorn thicket.
Plant at 3m spacing

mature
oak

mature
oak

Path

10m

pond

Willow coppice, planted at 2m
spacing, divided into 2 coupes.
Cut one coupe each year

Oak, hornbeam
& ash to be grown
to maturity.
Understorey of
hazel & holly at
3m spacing

O

H

A

A

A

Hazel coppice, planted
at 3m spacing, divided
into 3 coupes. Cut one
coupe every 2 years in
rotation. Ash to be
grown to maturity

A

A

A

sweet
chestnut
coppice, planted
at 3m spacing,
divided into 2 coupes.
Cut one coupe every 6
years. Ash to be grown to
maturity

BARTLEY JUNIOR SCHOOL, HAMPSHIRE
Tree Planting Scheme

Planting methods

Information is given below on the following types of planting:

- Notch planting of bare-root plants

- Planting cell-grown plants

- Pit planting of bare-root plants

- Planting container-grown plants

- Direct planting of cuttings and sets

Note the following general rules:

- The roots of bare-root plants must be kept moist and covered at all times. Exposing the roots for only a few minutes can damage the fine root hairs, and reduce the plant's chance of survival. Keep the plants in the planting bag until the moment you are ready for planting.

- Don't dig holes or notches until the day of planting, or they are likely to fill with water. Normally it's best to dig the notch and plant the tree in one operation, but when working with groups of young school children for example, it may be more efficient if adults dig the notches and the children plant the trees.

- Don't soak or dip the roots of bare-root plants into water before you plant. This can damage the fine root hairs and nodules by washing off the protective layer of soil particles. Soaking young trees in water as a way of alleviating root damage from drying should never be needed, as the situation should not arise. If the plants arrive with dry roots, advise the nursery immediately. The damage caused to roots by loss of moisture is anyway not reversed by rewetting. An exception to this rule is if you are using a mycorrhizal or other root dip, which is used just before planting (p71), and coats the damp root hairs with a fine gel.

- Watering the tree immediately after planting, even with a small amount of water, is beneficial. If possible use about a bucketful per plant.

- The planting notches or holes must be big enough to take the roots, so no roots are bent or broken. The main roots stay in the position in which they are planted, so make sure they are spread evenly, and are not cramped or bent.

- A bare-root plant should be put in to the same depth as it was growing previously, as shown by the soil mark on the root collar. If not planted deep enough, the plant will be poorly anchored with roots exposed. Planting too deeply may cause the base of the stem to rot.

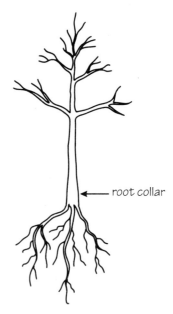

root collar

- The stems should be vertical to encourage well-balanced growth with a strong, upright base to the stem. If vertical the young trees are also more readily visible so reducing the chance of them being trodden on or omitted during weeding operations.

- After planting, tread firmly and carefully around the young plant to securely anchor the roots. Take care not to scrape the bark with your boot, and in clay soils don't stamp so hard that you make a depression around the stem, as this will tend to collect water and cause the stem to rot.

- Check for firmness by gently pulling on the stem, and the plant should not loosen. All the plants should be checked again at least once in the three or four weeks after planting, and firmed in again as necessary. Also check after heavy winds or frosts, and again just before the plants come into growth in the spring.

Protect and weed the trees after planting (see pp82-92 and chapter 7).

NOTCH PLANTING

Notch planting is usually the best method for young bare-root trees on most sites. Stock with very spreading roots may need to be pit planted (p79), or a 'hybrid' system may be appropriate (p79). Trees should not be notch planted direct into heavy clay soils without previous soil preparation (p69).

The planting notch is best made with a heavy, straight bladed garden spade, or a special planting spade (see chapter 4).

The basic method is very simple. Push the blade into the ground and then use a backwards and forwards movement to open a notch as shown. Then with a sideways, wiping motion, slide the plant into position and pull it upwards slightly to spread the roots. Then tread firmly and carefully around the stem to close the notch.

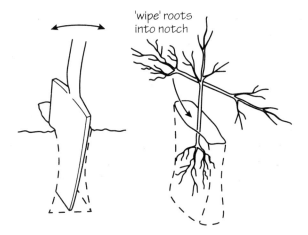

Don't push the plant straight down or you will bend the roots upwards and probably break some of them.

You may need to adjust the depth of the notch according to the length of the roots. Don't make a deeper notch than necessary, as even if you close the notch at the surface, you may leave an air pocket in which the roots are suspended and dry out.

Except for very small plants, you should make two cuts in different directions, following a 'T' plan as shown. This breaks up a larger volume of soil below the surface, giving space to spread the roots.

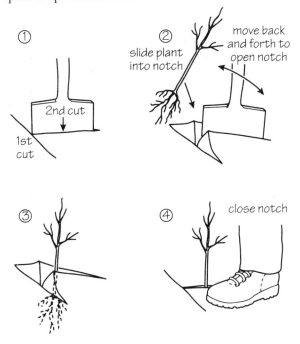

Planting in grass

In general when planting into fertile grassland, much the best way is to plant direct into the grass sward, and then after planting, kill off an area 1m square around each tree with herbicide or plastic sheet mulch, and maintain it as a weed-free area. If the whole sward is killed off by herbicide or cultivated before the trees are planted, there will be a strong growth of weeds which will be much more difficult to control than the original grass sward.

If you are going to use a herbicide after tree planting, the notch can be made straight into the turf. The cut can be easily made through short or sparse turf, and in crumbly soil the turf can be quite helpful in stopping the notch collapsing as you dig.

It is more difficult to make the slits through long, tough grass, as the blade will not cut through so easily. Consider mowing the grass in the late summer before planting, so that you start with short turf. If you are planning to use herbicide, spraying is also easier and more effective on short, new grass than on longer, older growth.

If it's too difficult to cut through the turf, you may need to remove a couple of turves at the planting position, and plant into the bare ground (called screef planting). Depending on how they come up, the turves can either be broken up and discarded, or laid grass side down around the planted tree. In damper ground, a thick turf can be removed and inverted, and the tree is then planted into the turf (called turf planting). This gives a better drained planting position to improve root growth and survival. The inverted turves are not effective as a method of weed control, and herbicide or mulches will be needed.

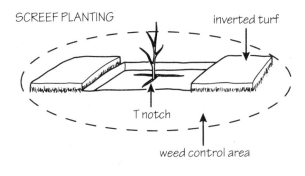

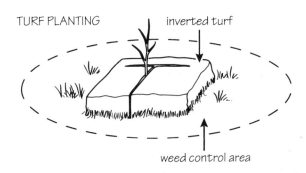

If you don't want to use either herbicide or mulch for weed control, you will need to start with a generous weed-free area, and maintain it by hand weeding or hoeing. An area with sides equivalent to four spades width is not too big, although it may look so when you plant! You must weed. Even if you mow the grass around the planting square, by mid-summer it will have partly grown over with grass or been invaded with other weeds, adversely affecting tree growth and survival. This method of weed control is not generally recommended, as it is easy to damage the stem or roots of the tree when using a hoe or fork.

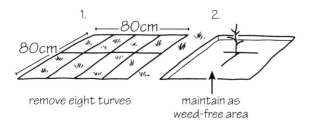

remove eight turves | maintain as weed-free area

If planting individual or small groups of trees in parks, gardens or school grounds which have existing shrub beds or borders, plant the trees in the beds rather than in the grass, as they will establish much more quickly (p27). As required, it is easy to convert beds to grass or vice versa once the trees are established.

Planting in machine cultivated ground

Where heavy clay soils have been ploughed to reduce compaction, ridges will be formed. Planting trees on the ridges will normally be beneficial as this provides a better drained planting position.

Where compacted ground has been loosened by ripping or subsoiling, it's usually best not to plant along the rip line, as this tends to open up in dry weather. Although it's tempting to use the rip line as a ready-made planting line, it's usually best to make new notches between the rip lines (p69).

CELL-GROWN PLANTS

Cell-grown plants are grown in special small containers designed for tree seedlings, which promote good root growth without 'spiralling' (p47). They can be planted earlier in the autumn than bare-root stock, and can establish without check and make late autumn root growth. Compared to bare-root stock, the use of cell-grown plants therefore reduces the pressure to get all planting done in the late autumn/early winter period. In early autumn the days are longer, and the weather and ground conditions are usually better than later in the year, making the job more pleasant, and causing less damage to the ground. Cell-grown plants should be planted well before bud-burst in spring, to allow roots to grow into the surrounding soil before water is lost through the new foliage. The best time to plant is September. Cell-grown trees can be planted between July and October, but planting in the earlier months will normally require regular watering.

Due to the lack of check at planting, the relative height growth of cell-grown plants is better than bare-root stock in the year following planting.

Various sizes of cell are produced, to suit various species and uses (p47).

Cell-grown plants are best planted as soon as possible after delivery, to save possible deterioration during storage. Immediately on delivery, they should be stored outside in a sheltered position. If trees are in leaf and planting is delayed, regular checks must be made to ensure that the root plugs are kept moist. The supplier will give advice on storage and watering, as this will vary according to the method of packing.

Note the following:

• Cell-grown plants can be planted with an ordinary spade, but a special tool called a 'spear' makes planting easier and quicker.

• Whatever tool is used, the top of the cell or plug must be at least 12mm (half an inch) below the soil surface, and covered with soil. If it's exposed, the compost in the cell dries out and does not easily re-wet.

• Various plant boxes and carriers are available from suppliers of cell-grown plants, to ease the job of planting.

• In heavy clays, cell-grown plants should not be planted without previous soil preparation, such as deep cultivation or ripping.

Specialist tools for planting cell-grown plants are like spades, but instead of a blade have a 'spear', which makes a hole of the correct size for planting. They can be used in any soil except very sandy soil, and can be used to penetrate stony ground. In clay soils a twisting motion should be used to tear the side of the hole, as otherwise 'smeared' sides can be formed which are difficult for the roots to penetrate.

Plant as follows:

1 Insert the spear vertically, and then push it back and forth slightly. Twist it through 180° and remove. In heavy clay it may be necessary to make a second cut at 90° to the first cut and then twist again.

2 Carefully position a plant in the hole, so that the top of the plug is 12mm (half an inch) below the soil surface. There must be good contact between the sides of the plug and the soil, so that the plug does not dry out.

3 Insert the spear again about 5cm (2") from the plant, and pull the handle towards you, so that the spear firms the soil at the base of the plug. Then push the handle away from you to firm the soil at the top of the plug.

4 Cover the top of the plug with a handful of soil. Gently firm around the plant, being careful not to damage it with your boot.

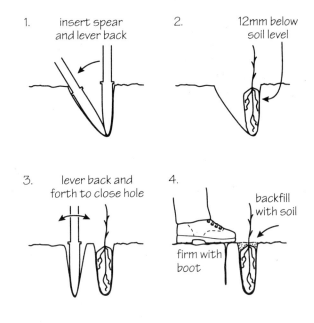

1. insert spear and lever back

2. 12mm below soil level

3. lever back and forth to close hole

4. backfill with soil / firm with boot

PIT PLANTING

Pit planting is considered by some to be the better way of planting, because the soil is removed, broken up, and replaced around the roots. However, with small, vigorous transplants there is little advantage in digging a pit, which is slower and harder work than making a notch. Young tree roots are very strong, and have no problem penetrating most soils as long as the tree is not having to compete for water or nutrients. However, notch planting which is poorly done, with roots crammed into too small a space, or with notches not closed properly, will result in losses.

In many situations a 'hybrid' method works well. One person cuts through the turf and digs out a sod of earth which is kept on the spade, resting on the ground by the hole. Another person places the tree in position and spreads the roots, while the first person crumbles the soil back into the hole. With experience, one person can do this on their own by tipping the soil gently off the spade whilst holding the tree in the other hand, although it needs strength in the wrist to hold the laden spade! This method is nearly as fast as notch planting.

Pit planting (see below) is recommended in the following situations:

• Where the young tree has roots which are too bushy and spreading to fit in a T notch. Some species produce bushy roots even at the seedling or one year stage. Larger and older bare-root plants will tend to have more bushy roots.

• In clay soils (see below)

• In very friable, crumbly soils such as cultivated garden soil, in which a notch tends to collapse so you end up digging a hole anyway.

• For container-grown plants other than cell-grown stock.

Pit planting should not be used as an alternative to whole site ground preparation. For example, on wet clays, if you simply dig a pit without generally improving drainage, the pit will fill with water and the tree roots will 'drown'.

When pit-planting bare-root stock it is not generally necessary to add any organic matter such as compost or manure (p70). Additional organic matter may be helpful when planting container-grown stock (see below).

Clay soils

Clay soils are a problem. If you cut a notch, the sides of the notch are smeared by the spade producing a surface which is difficult for roots to penetrate. The notch itself may re-open in dry weather when the clay shrinks. If you dig a pit, this can become waterlogged in wet weather, creating anaerobic conditions that kill the roots. Adding compost or other soil improvers can worsen this tendency for the pit to become waterlogged and anaerobic.

In some clay soils, you may be able to break up the subsoil at the bottom of the pit, ensuring that water drains through freely. On other sites, the whole tree planting area will need deep ripping or ploughing in order to break up the clay (ref to p69).

Clay soils are also a problem when it comes to maintaining bare ground around each tree (p97), as the bare ground tends to crack in dry conditions, exposing tree roots to drying. A thick layer of organic mulch, renewed annually, will help prevent this.

Procedure

To pit plant a tree:

1 When planting in grass, you will need first to remove some turf. If you are going to use herbicide or mulch for weed control, you need only remove sufficient turves to dig the pit. The turves can be inverted around the pit, or set aside and then inverted in the original position after planting. Alternatively they can be chopped up in the bottom of the pit. If you are going to hand weed, a much bigger area of turf must be removed (p78).

2 Dig a pit large enough to take the tree roots or rootball, putting the soil to one side. If the topsoil and subsoil are noticeably different, keep them separate. You can put the soil on a plastic sheet for easy retrieval. Discard any

large stones. Dig the hole square, rather than round (see next section).

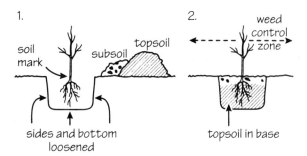

3 In cohesive soils, loosen the soil in the sides and bottom of the pit with a spade or fork. In crumbly soils don't touch the sides or they will collapse, and you'll have to start again!

4 Working quickly but carefully, place the tree in the pit, spreading the roots, and checking that the soil collar is at the correct height (p76). Adjust as necessary, by adding or taking away more soil. If working as a pair, the other person then backfills carefully around the roots, using the most friable soil first. Shake the tree gently so the soil trickles through the roots and any air spaces are filled. Then use the remaining soil to fill the pit, finishing it level with the surrounding soil. Firm the soil with your hands or feet, but don't stamp hard around the tree or you are likely to both over-compact the soil and scrape the bark of the stem.

5 Water the tree if possible.

CONTAINER-GROWN PLANTS

Evergreen species of tree, including the native holly, yew and box do not transplant successfully bare-root, and have to be grown in pots or other containers (p47). Garden centres and other outlets sell a huge variety of other container-grown trees and shrubs, for all year round sales and planting. For conservation and amenity purposes, container-grown plants should only be used for the native evergreens, for particular garden cultivars that are only available this way, and for the occasional ceremonial planting which can't be done during the normal planting season!

Most container-grown plants are grown in composts mainly comprising peat, although composted bark, coir and other organic materials may be used. These are light, clean materials which promote rapid root growth, but can make it difficult for the plant roots to adapt to the surrounding soil. The rootball may also have a different type of water-holding ability, so that the surrounding soil can be fairly moist, while the peaty rootball dries out and does not easily re-absorb water. When planting, cover the top of the rootball with a layer of soil to prevent the rootball acting

like a wick and evaporating moisture from the compost and soil. If a rootball of peat compost has dried out, it can be rewetted by watering with a solution of about 5 ml of washing-up liquid in 5 litres of water.

For these reasons, it is important to cultivate a larger volume of soil when planting container-grown plants, and to mix soil improvers such as compost or leaf mould into the soil backfill. The main purpose of these is to make an even gradation between the compost in the rootball and the surrounding soil, so that roots can more easily make the transition.

Research has shown that plants do better in square pits, rather than round. This is because when new roots meet the junction of the backfill and the side of the pit, they tend to curve round and follow the side, especially if they have already been growing spirally in a container. This tendency is increased if the backfill is markedly different from the surrounding soil. However, on meeting the corner of a square hole the roots are reluctant to turn a right angle, and instead break out into the surrounding soil.

Plants should always be removed from the container, even if the container is meant to be biodegradable, to ease the passage of roots into the new ground.

Procedure

1 Make sure the compost in the container is thoroughly watered. If it has been allowed to become dry, you will need to rewet it as described above, or stand it in water for an hour or so until water has been reabsorbed right through the rootball. If put in the ground dry, the compost of the rootball does not easily re-wet.

2 Remove the turf as described above.

3 Dig a square hole about twice the volume of the container, and pile the soil neatly to the side, keeping topsoil and subsoil separate.

4 Put some compost or other organic matter into the hole and mix it in with some of the saved topsoil, bringing it up to about the level of the base of the pot. You can check this by putting the plant in the hole, still in the container, and then adjusting the amount of soil as necessary.

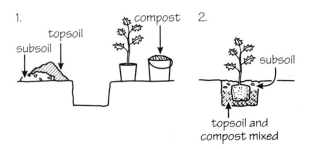

5   Remove the plant from its container. If the roots are at all coiled around in the shape of the pot, you should gently loosen them and prise them out, or they may continue to grow around in that shape. If it's very firm, loosen the sides of the rootball with your fingers. If the roots are very badly coiled and are impossible to prise out, this shows that the plant has been kept too long in the container, and is potbound. Any plants like this should be rejected and returned to the supplier.

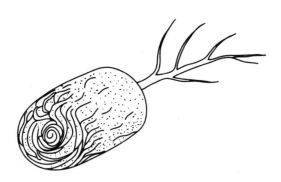

6   Place the plant in the hole with the top of the rootball just below the surrounding soil, and backfill with the remaining topsoil and subsoil. Cover the top of the rootball with topsoil. Tread gently to firm the plant into position. Water it thoroughly.

STAKING

The aim should be to use small, young trees which do not require staking, and which will establish faster than larger trees. Stakes and ties add to the cost of the scheme, and the maintenance requirement.

However, whips and standard trees (see table on page 68) may sometimes need to be planted, perhaps where a particular species or cultivar is only available in that size. Avoid planting this size when the only reason is for instant impact (p66). Smaller whips need not always be staked, although this may help protect them from accidental damage on some sites. Standard trees will need to be staked against movement by the wind, but only a short stake should be used, with a fairly loose tie. The reason is that the flexing of the tree in the wind stimulates root growth to naturally brace the tree, and also stimulates growth in stem diameter at the base of the trunk. If the tree is so tightly staked that it cannot sway, this natural bracing does not develop, and it is then very likely to snap or be blown over when the stake and tie are removed.

If you must use a standard tree, stake it as described below. Don't use a taller stake than is necessary (see point 2 below). Stakes pressure-treated with preservative are not required, as the stake only has to last about two seasons. However, if the stake is also being used to support a tree guard, a hardwood or preserved softwood stake may be advisable (p88). Don't use stakes of imported hardwood.

1   Plant the tree as normal (p79), but don't completely backfill the pit.

2   Knock the stake into the bottom of the pit, on the windward side of the tree, as close as possible to the rootball without damaging it. The stake should finish at a height no more than one third of the height of the tree. Backfill the hole.

3   Loosely attach the tree to the stake, using a proprietary tree tie. Many different types of tie are available, so check with the supplier if you are not sure of the correct way of fitting. Ties should form a figure of eight or have a spacer between the tree and the stake, to prevent chafing. Most ties will need nailing to the stake to stop them slipping, unless they can be fitted just above a branch. Buckle ends should be against the stake, not the tree, and should normally be nailed. Check the tree and stake frequently, and remove the tie at the beginning of the second growing season, by which time the tree should be securely anchored by its roots. If it's not, then the tree is not growing sufficiently well, and other steps (chapter 7) will need to be taken to encourage the tree into growth.

Double stakes can also be used, as shown in the diagram. These are more reliable and less likely to cause chafing. They also act as protectors against careless mowing, which is a significant cause of damage to young trees.

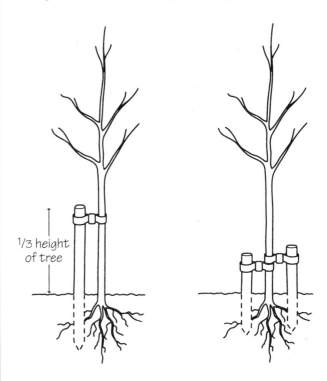

1/3 height of tree

For container-grown or rootballed trees, an angled stake can be used to avoid damaging the rootball. Angle the stake at 45°, positioned away from the prevailing wind so it is not loosened by the action of the wind on the tree.

PLANTING CUTTINGS AND SETS

The simplest way to plant a tree is to insert a cutting into the ground. This works well for willow and poplar, as described on page 61. This method is widely used in nurseries for propagation of willows and poplars, and can also be used for planting direct into the final planting position.

Cuttings should be 20-25cm (8-10") long and 1-2cm (1/2") diameter. Make a hole at the planting position with a bar or similar, of a diameter just greater than that of the cutting. The hole should be about 2-3cm (1") shorter than the cutting. Don't use the cutting itself to make the hole. Insert the cutting, so that about 2-3cm (1") is protruding, from where the first bud will grow. Tread in firmly, to ensure they fit snugly.

Note the following:

• The ground must be suitable for the species. Willow and poplar grow best in wet or moist soils.

• As with planting a young tree, the planting position should be clear of weeds, with at least a metre square kept clear of weeds for at least two growing seasons.

Although the size of cuttings or sets is normally as recommended above, much larger, thicker 'cuttings' can regrow. Even fencing stakes of willow, freshly cut and untreated, will regrow if set in the ground the same way up as they were growing!

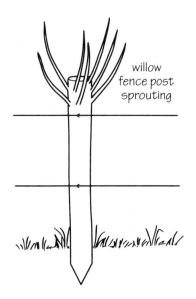

willow fence post sprouting

Using willow cuttings can be a useful way of establishing tree growth in areas prone to vandalism. As desired, other species can then be planted amongst the willows to create a mixed woodland. This should be done within one or two years, as willow grows very fast and it will get increasingly difficult to establish other trees amongst them.

Tree protection

Tree protection is an important part of tree planting on many sites, and must be planned carefully from the outset. Tree protection materials are expensive, and often cost more than the trees themselves. However, without proper protection, most planting will be a waste of time and resources. Tree protection may also be needed to protect young trees which have naturally regenerated.

On urban sites, protection against stock and wild animals may be unnecessary. Proper public consultation and appropriate planting design is likely to be more effective than fencing or other protection against people, which may attract vandalism (*The Urban Handbook*, BTCV, 1998). Many urban woodlands have been successfully established in recent years with no tree protection at all.

Any of the following agents may cause damage to young trees. They are discussed further below (p83-86). Animals cause damage by bark-stripping, which weakens the tree. Animals also 'browse' on trees, which means to eat the leaves and young shoots. Larger animals can trample and uproot young trees.

• Wild animals. These include voles, rabbits, hares, and deer. You will need to find out which of these are present in the area, and what the level of threat is likely to be.

• Stock. These include sheep, cattle, horses and goats. Check any planned uses for grazing land for the few years after planting. Adequate protection against sheep, for example, would not be sufficient against horses. This can be difficult to plan, as changes are often made at short notice.

• People. Young trees can be damaged accidentally, for example by people trampling them, or they can be vandalised. Consultation with local people is an important part of planning tree planting. A lot of damage is also caused by careless mowing, brushcutting and strimming by mowing contractors or ground maintenance staff.

• Wind. Strong winds are damaging to young trees, not only because of physical damage to tender leaves, shoots and stems, but because of the drying effect of the wind, which reduces the humidity around the tree. Treeshelters (p87) were originally designed to increase the humidity around the tree, but are also useful against some of the agents mentioned above.

There are various types of protection, some of which can protect against more than one of the agents given above. You need to select the type of protection which will be effective against the most agents, will not have unwanted side effects such as attracting vandalism, and will be cost effective. The method of weed control being planned can also affect the choice of tree protector. For example, tree shelters have the useful side effect of protecting the young tree from being damaged by herbicide spray.

Trees can either be protected individually, or as a group, or a combination of methods can be used.

A large number of different products are available, including those listed below. All the products are available in a range of heights to suit various purposes. Further details are given below (p87)

- Vole or strimmer guards

- Spiral guards, opaque and transparent

- Wire or plastic mesh guards

- Tree shelters

- Metal surrounds

- Timber tree surrounds. Normally built from standard fencing materials.

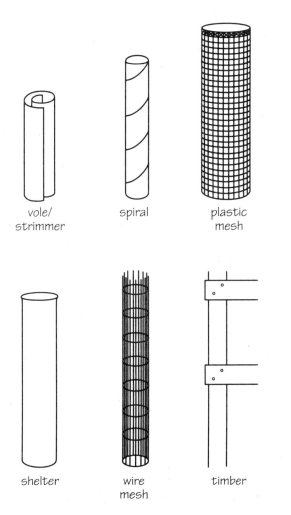

vole/strimmer   spiral   plastic mesh

shelter   wire mesh   timber

The following methods can be used to protect groups of trees. They can be used instead of, or in addition to, individual protection.

- Fencing of planted area.

- Chemical deterrents.

- Control of animals causing damage.

See page 86 for details on the choice between individual protection or fences.

Stock and wild animals can not only damage trees, but also may hinder the development of a diverse shrub layer and ground flora. In existing woods, high numbers of deer can seriously affect the value of existing ground vegetation. On the other hand, lower grazing densities can promote diversity and keep glades open. When considering tree protection, the management of the wood in the longer term also needs to be considered.

WILD ANIMALS

In order to make a suitable choice of protection, you need to know the likelihood of damage occurring. This means finding out about which of the 'pest' species are in the area, and what the level of threat is likely to be. Talk to others responsible for tree planting and management in your area, to farmers, and to your local Forestry Commission officer. If you are planning to rely on natural regeneration as a way of rejuvenating a woodland, protection against wild animals and stock will be essential.

Voles

The field or short-tailed vole is probably the most widespread and numerous British mammal. It is 10cm (4") long, short-tailed, brown with grey below, and lives in hedges, rough grassland, the borders of woodlands and in gardens. In plantations of young trees the population can quickly grow to plague proportions of around 500 per acre, causing damage to stems and young shoots up to about 5cm (2") in diameter. Populations tend to be higher following a mild winter. Normally, voles live mainly on grass, often biting off long stems at ground level.

Field voles are most likely to cause problems where there is long grass to give cover. Mulch materials such as bark or plastic sheeting can also provide cover. This in turn can lead to problems where foxes tear at the plastic mulch in order to get at the voles! Mainly in winter, the voles gnaw the bark away just above the soil level, typically leaving a bare strip on which tiny teeth marks, about 1mm wide and in pairs, can just be seen. They can also gnaw the roots below ground level. If you part the surrounding mat of grass, you'll find a complex system of vole runways and parlours, with vole droppings and small piles of grass stems cut into short lengths. Damage can also occur beneath snow.

Use of herbicide which leaves a bare patch around the base of the stem discourages voles by removing their cover. Otherwise, guards will be needed on grassy sites. Where populations are high, voles will cross bare ground. The worst damage occurs when populations reach 'superabundant' numbers, which happens on a three to five yearly cycle in suitable grassy habitats. The base of the vole guard or treeshelter (see note page 87) must be buried at least 5mm into the soil. Spiral guards with ventilation holes are not effective.

Voles are food for birds of prey, with kestrels and barn owls in particular likely to hunt over areas of long grassland. Where the site lacks high trees or posts for perching, you may be able to encourage some of these birds to hunt over a newly planted woodland by providing perching positions. If you can erect them safely, a couple of 'telegraph pole' size posts with a 'wire' between may be just the job! Pole-mounted barn owl and kestrel nesting boxes require quite an investment of time and resources, but have proved very successful in encouraging these birds of prey into young tree plantations. See Dewar Shawyer (1996) for further details.

Rabbits and hares

Rabbits are common in many parts of Britain, with hares locally common in suitable habitats. Rabbits graze mainly on grass, but outside the breeding season can survive on bark and shoots of trees and bushes. Damage is most severe in winter and early spring, especially during snow when other food is scarce. Snow also gives access higher up the stems. Rabbits are likely to be absent from areas where there are high numbers of urban foxes, where myxomatosis is present, and in very wet terrain.

Rabbits require dry shelter within about 400m of grazing. They can breed anytime between January and August, and numbers can increase very rapidly in suitable habitats. To check for rabbits, look for droppings or freshly used burrows within a 400m radius of the planned tree planting area. Total exclusion of rabbits using rabbit fencing is usually too expensive for conservation planting. Extermination of rabbits is a specialist job. Rabbits thrive in cover such as thickets of bramble, elder, hedgerows, and on banks and piles of rubble, which are just the sort of habitat the conservationist usually wants to keep and increase!

Browsing damage by rabbits and hares can be distinguished from browsing by deer, because rabbits and hares make a clean, usually oblique cut and often leave the severed shoot on the ground. Deer leave a ragged cut, and eat the shoot. Bark damage by rabbits and hares is usually from ground level up to 50cm (20"), but may be higher after snow. The damaged area shows a diagonal pattern of teeth marks, with the width of each tooth mark less than 3.2mm. Smooth barked trees are preferred, with ash and cherry favourites, whilst alder may be ignored. Compared to vole damage, the damage is higher up the stem, always above the level of the grass mat, and is not so concentrated in one patch, so that areas of bark remain between the gnawed strips.

Damage by browsing and bark stripping can occur up until the trees are about eight years old, but sometimes even the thick bark at the base of semi-mature trees may be attacked.

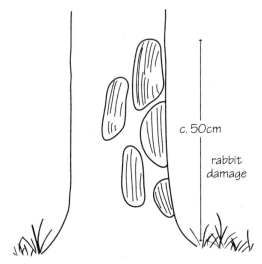

Hares can be damaging in commercial plantations, but are unlikely to cause problems in conservation or amenity plantings. Their favoured habitat is open grassland, with one hare per two hectares a high population, but they can cause damage where they use woodlands for shelter.

Trees can be protected against rabbits and hares by various guards (see table below) or by fencing (p51). Where populations of rabbits are high, specialist help with live trapping or gassing may be necessary.

Deer

There are seven species of deer living wild in Britain, of which two, red and roe, are native. Most areas of Britain have one or more species well established. Fallow deer are fairly common throughout lowland England, with roe deer common in southern England, and in most of Scotland. Sika, muntjac and chinese water deer have spread from various parks and are common in certain localities. There are probably more deer in Britain today than at any time in the past.

Deer cause damage to young trees by browsing on the shoots, especially between January and May, when the shoots are tender and other food may be scarce. Browsing damage can occur though at any time of year. Young trees browsed by deer develop many leading shoots, or if severely browsed, form small, clipped bushes. Cherry is particularly palatable to deer, followed by ash and willow, whereas they dislike alder, birch and walnut. Taller shelters than those normally recommended against particular species of deer may be needed for the more palatable tree species.

The vulnerability to being browsed will depend on other food available, but likely targets are:

• Recently planted trees, especially if planted in clearings where deer are accustomed to graze. There is some evidence that planted trees are more palatable than natural seedlings, which may be due to the increased nitrogen content from use of fertiliser in the tree nursery.

• Young trees surrounded by thicket-stage plantings, scrub or bushes, which give cover and shelter.

Browsing by deer not only causes immediate damage, but delays the time by which leading shoots grow beyond their reach, so in the worst cases, the trees never 'get away'.

The smaller deer, roe and muntjac, can cause damage by fraying the stems of young trees with their antlers. Fraying by roe deer occurs for several months before the rut, and can cause scattered damage to a developing woodland.

Trees can be protected from deer by guards (see table below), chemical repellents or perimeter fencing. Electric fencing has not been found effective for more than very short-term protection. Roe deer are virtually immune to electric shocks! For the longer term management of woodland, control of deer populations in association with a local Deer Management Group is likely to be the best method. Contact your local Forestry Commission office for advice.

Squirrels

Squirrels do not damage newly planted trees, but affect which species you should choose to plant as they can severely damage established smooth-barked trees, of between 8 and 30 years age, by bark stripping. It is not worth planting beech or sycamore if the local squirrel population is high. Oak and sweet chestnut may also be attacked, while ash, cherry or walnut are usually not touched. Bark stripping is thought to be caused by males with insufficient territory. Fencing and tree guards are ineffective, and control by poisoning or live trapping is the only method, preferably in association with a local Squirrel Management Group. Contact your local Forestry Commission Office for advice. Control measures should aim for a small number of dominant males to keep out invaders, as eradication will only cause others to move in to the territory. See chapter 7.

STOCK

Cattle, sheep, horses, goats and other stock do not mix with young trees. Even where there is plenty of grass to eat, stock are always curious, and will tend to nibble most things within reach. They will also trample young plants, use stakes and guards as rubbing posts and strip the bark. Stock will seek the shelter and shade of young trees, trampling them and compacting the ground around the trees, impeding drainage and causing damage to roots.

Tree guards, surrounds and fences around young woodlands must be designed to exclude stock in adjacent pastures, as detailed in the tables on page 87. Any structure must be substantial and soundly built, as stock will lean on the surround to reach inside to browse and graze, and rub themselves against posts and rails. Goats and some sheep will also put their feet up on rails or netting in order to reach higher to browse.

When selecting the type of guard or fence, consider the general state of fencing in the area. Particularly when grazing is in short supply, animals on neighbouring land may break out through inadequate fencing and stray onto land where they have access to your trees, and cause damage in a matter of hours. It is the legal duty of the neighbour to control his/her stock, but it may be prudent to take precautions against the loss of several years' tree growth.

PEOPLE

In some situations and communities, there will be no need to protect young trees from accidental or purposeful damage. Some sites will require protection, while in other situations protection may actually draw attention to the trees, making them more vulnerable to vandalism. Elaborate tree surrounds may be seen as a challenge for people to get through, take apart or torch. Sometimes larger trees are respected more than small transplants, while in other places larger trees may get snapped off while smaller ones are ignored.

Consultation

Consultation with local people is vital at an early stage in planning any tree planting. It's not just a matter of 'winning people over to your point of view', but allowing locals to take a real part in putting forward ideas, forming plans and taking a practical part in planting and management. See *The Urban Handbook* (BTCV, 1998) for further discussion.

Guards

Vole guards, spiral rabbit guards and treeshelters make trees more easily visible so they are less likely to be trampled or mown accidentally, although this visibility can also attract unwanted attention. They have no effect against accidental damage from children playing football for example, or against vandalism.

Plastic or wire mesh guards protect against trampling and mowing damage, and prevent direct damage to the stems and bark of trees. Plastic guards are easier to vandalise than wire mesh guards.

Rigid metal tree guards are expensive, but may be appropriate for trees in parks, pavements and pedestrianised areas.

Post and rail or post and netting surrounds will be respected in many communities, but in some areas may be vandalised, torched or stolen. Chestnut paling is difficult to climb and awkward to take apart, but can be quite easily stolen or cut away in sections.

Other methods

The planting design and method of management in the early years will have an effect on people's perception of the planting, and its susceptibility to vandalism. When planting areas of formerly mown grass, the simplest and most effective method for successful establishment and weed control is to plant direct into the sward, and then use a herbicide. However, this may draw unwanted attention to the young trees. Instead, it may be better to let the grass grow up long, until the area is perceived as a piece of rough ground, and then plant shrub and tree species amongst it. The conditions of shelter, shade and higher humidity may physically benefit the young trees on otherwise exposed sites, as well as hiding and protecting them from unwanted attention. On the other hand, some residents may view this type of planting as untidy and unkempt.

FENCES OR GUARDS?

The cost of individual tree protection increases directly with the number of trees protected, whereas the cost of fencing relates to the size and shape of the land enclosed, regardless of the number of trees enclosed. On average, as the size of the tree planting area increases above 1 hectare (2.47 acres), fencing becomes proportionally less expensive than individual protection. For areas below 1 hectare (2.47 acres), individual protection is normally cheaper. However, choice should always be made by making separate costings and comparing them. Fencing costs are affected by the shape of the enclosed area, the number of strainers needed and other factors. Individual protection depends on the total number of trees and for any given area, varies according to the spacing of the trees.

Perimeter fencing against deer or rabbits should be considered for:

- Areas over 1 hectare (2.47 acres).

- Areas with trees planted at 2.1m spacing (2250 per hectare).

- Plantings which include conifers, as these are particularly vulnerable to deer damage.

- Areas which have valuable woodland flora and high deer populations. Deer, and especially muntjac, can cause severe browsing damage to bluebells, primroses, orchids, dog's mercury and other species.

Perimeter fencing can be a disadvantage in blocking routes for wildlife or restricting the passage of game birds. Badgers can be catered for by constructing a badger gate. Fences should also not be built across deer 'runs', as deer will continue to try and use the run, damaging themselves and the fence.

Fences restrict public access to woodland. This restriction may be useful in the establishment phase, but may be less appropriate as the woodland matures and its recreational potential increases. In the long term, light grazing of woodland by stock or wild animals can promote diversity. It may be appropriate to remove the fencing once the woodland is established.

In large woodlands it may be possible to fence areas in rotation to use grazing, browsing and trampling as agents to manage natural regeneration and other aspects of woodland development.

For full details of stock, rabbit and deer fencing, and badger gates, see *Fencing* (BTCV, 1986). Note that electric line fences against rabbits and deer are only suitable for temporary protection. For long term protection, fences of rabbit netting or deer netting to a suitable specification must be used.

PRODUCTS, MATERIALS AND TECHNIQUES

General points:

- There is a huge range of products available, with new ones being added each year. Well-tried and tested products are usually the best choice.

- Choose environmentally-sound products, for example those which do not contain pvc. Some products are made from recycled plastic.

- However well protected, weed control is still vital for at least the first three years. Make sure that weeds do not get established inside the guard or shelter, and keep at least a 1m diameter weed-free circle around the tree.

- Check at least annually, to make sure the shelter is not restricting tree growth. Many shelters are now made with perforated lines which split as the tree grows.

Table 6c is a guide to the heights required against different species. There is no point in using a guard that is taller than necessary, as this will involve extra expense, although taller guards may be necessary on steeply sloping ground. Nearly all manufacturers of tree protection products use these heights as standard. Note that treeshelters and plastic mesh tree guards are not sturdy enough to withstand cattle or horses.

Table 6c: Heights of treeshelters and guards

ANIMAL	HEIGHT OF GUARD
Vole	20cm
Rabbit	60cm
Hare	75cm
Roe and muntjac deer	1.2m
Sheep (small breeds)	1.5m
Sheep (large breeds)	1.8m
Red, sika and fallow deer	1.8m

Table 6d (below) gives a guide to some of the products available, and their uses. Most are available in a range of heights and diameters. The choice depends on the size and bushiness of the stock being planted, as well as the animals to protect against. The products are described further below.

Treeshelters

Treeshelters were originally developed as 'mini-greenhouses', to increase survival and growth rates on newly planted trees, by lessening the stresses caused by transplanting. Growth can be from two to five times the normal rate in the first few years. Treeshelters are also useful to:

- Reduce the losses caused by mammals, including browsing, bark stripping and fraying.

- Reduce damage by strimmers, brushcutters and mowers. Care still needs to be taken that the machine does not damage the shelter.

- Make trees easy to spot amongst tall vegetation, so speeding maintenance.

Table 6d: Tree protection products

PRODUCT	SUITABLE FOR:	PROTECT AGAINST:	ENHANCE GROWTH
Treeshelters	Small transplants and cell-grown seedlings	All wild animals except for voles*, sheep	Yes
Quills	Single-stemmed transplants, hedging	Voles, rabbits	Yes
Gro-cones	Small transplants and cell-grown seedlings	Voles, rabbits, hares, roe deer	Yes
Shrubshelters	Multi-stemmed planting stock	Voles and rabbits	Yes, but less than narrow shelters
Shelterguards	Small transplants and cell-grown seedlings	All wild animals, sheep	Yes
Spiral guards	Large transplants, at least 15cm taller than guard	Rabbits and hares	No
Vole and strimmer guards	Established trees	Voles and strimmers	No
Plastic mesh guards	All young trees	All wild animals, sheep	No
Steel mesh guards	High value trees in vandal-prone sites	Deer, stock, people	No
Mild steel guards	High value trees in vandal-prone sites	Deer, stock, people	No
Timber guards	Trees in pastures	Stock, deer	No

* Treeshelters are normally proof against voles, provided they are buried at least 5mm into the ground and securely staked. Occasionally voles may gnaw through the treeshelter.

- Reduce the cost of herbicide application, by making it quicker and easier to spray or apply granules around the tree without damaging it.

There are also disadvantages to treeshelters:

- They are conspicuous, and can attract vandalism.

- On windy, exposed sites, the leading shoots are often badly damaged once they grow above the top of the shelter. Roadside plantings can suffer similar damage from the slipstream of passing lorries.

- Treeshelters accelerate early height growth, but stem diameter and root growth do not increase proportionally. If shelters are removed too early, the young tree will not be able to support itself.

- Treeshelters are not recommended for protecting beech, as this can be severely damaged by the beech woolly aphid, which thrives in the humid conditions inside the shelter.

- As the base of the stem thickens it can fill the shelter. If the shelter doesn't split, rainwater can get trapped and kill a ring of bark, so killing the tree.

- Weed growth inside the shelter will be enhanced, which may choke the young tree.

- Treeshelters must not be seen as the panacea of tree planting. A treeshelter will not make up for poor quality plants, careless planting or inattention to weeding.

Where there is no threat to the trees from animals, the extra expense of treeshelters may not be justified in terms of improved growth and survival alone.

Treeshelters encourage faster growth by increasing the humidity around the leaves, and reducing transpiration and passive water loss from the ground inside the shelter. This is especially significant in the first spring after planting, when roots have not regrown after transplanting and are less able to absorb water. If there is a drought, losses of newly planted trees not in shelters can be high. However, temperatures are significantly higher in the shelter than outside, and this can be stressful to the young plant in mid-summer if new roots have not grown. It's therefore important that where shelters are used, trees are planted and shelters fitted in late autumn or very early spring, so that the roots have time to grow before high summer temperatures are experienced. Shelters must not be used to extend the tree planting season into late spring.

There is a wide range of satisfactory products on the market, in unobtrusive browns and greens. All have rounded or splayed tops to reduce chafing when the leading shoot emerges. The ties are fastened to the shelter in such a way that they cannot encircle the tree. Stakes are required to support and secure the shelter (quills excepted). The stakes must not protrude above the top of the shelter, otherwise the leading shoots will chafe against the top of the stake. Suitable stakes are available from suppliers of treeshelters, normally either 20 x 20mm hardwood, or 25 x 25mm treated softwood, in lengths to suit the particular shelter. Hardwood is denser and stronger than softwood, so thinner stakes can be used.

Treeshelters are designed to break down under ultra-violet light after about five years, although in practice this does not always happen. In very shady or overgrown situations the shelters may not get sufficient light to cause disintegration, so they eventually restrict the growth of the trunk. Trees should be checked at least annually, and as necessary, shelters can be slit downwards with a knife, and then left in position for a couple more years to protect the bark against mammal damage. Some shelters have a perforated line so that the stem can break through as it expands.

Treeshelters will normally protect against voles, provided the shelter is pushed well down into the soil, so there is no gap at the base. Occasionally voles may nibble through the base of the shelter where populations are high. Treeshelters are not sturdy enough to protect against cattle or horses, as the treeshelter itself is likely to get damaged.

Shrubshelters are a similar product with a wider diameter, suitable for protecting multi-stemmed shrubs and trees. Compared to a treeshelter, the humidity difference inside the shelter is not so marked, due to the wider diameter of the tube, so growth enhancement is not so significant. Quills are self-supporting shelters, 60cm high, with a pointed base for easy insertion in the ground. They are suitable for hedging and other low-cost planting, and protect against voles and rabbits.

The procedure for planting and fitting shelters varies with the situation, product and personal preference, but the result should be a shelter which is upright, firmly attached, and with the base just below ground level. In theory one should knock in the stake first and then plant the tree, in order to ensure that the stake does not damage the roots. In practice, this can be quite awkward to do, as the stake is very close to the tree, leaving little room for making a notch. If you dig a pit, you must knock the stake in afterwards or you will dislodge it. When planting, position the main roots away from the windward point, where the stake will be knocked in.

1 If notch planting, remove the turf at the planting position so that weed growth is not encouraged inside the shelter. Alternatively, apply herbicide immediately after planting, and before fitting the shelter.

2 Plant the tree as described above.

3 Knock the stake in firmly on the windward side of the notch, at the correct distance from the tree to suit the particular shelter. Try and knock it in so that a flat side of the stake, not a corner, is against the shelter, so that the tie will not work loose. Alternatively put the shelter over first to aid positioning of the stake, and then one person holds the top of the shelter out of the way while another knocks in the stake. Another variation is to slide the tree root first into the shelter before planting, and then plant tree and shelter together! This can be the easier method if the tree is branching, or if the shelter has an internal stake loop, which tends to snag.

4 The top of the stake should finish about 5cm (2") above the upper tie on the shelter. It must not protrude above the top of the shelter, or the leading shoots will chafe against it when they emerge from the top of the shelter.

5 Fit the shelter over the tree, pushing the base into the ground. This prevent voles burrowing underneath, and for designs with only one tie, is important for holding it firm. Fasten the ties tightly.

Quills

The quill is a slim-diameter shelter with a pointed base, designed to be used without a stake. In friable soil, the base of the quill can be pushed about 15cm (6") into the ground without damage, which is sufficient to hold it securely in position. Quills are mainly used on hedging and other low-cost single-stemmed stock.

Gro-Cones

These treeshelters are slightly conical in shape, so they can be nested together for storage and transport. They are made of a net-reinforced transparent plastic, with a weld-line that splits as the stem fills the shelter. They should be fitted with the wider end uppermost, and can be supported by stakes, canes or steel rods.

Shrubshelters

These are strong, wide-diameter shelters for shrubs and other multi-stemmed plants. They need to be well anchored with stakes, as they offer greater resistance to the wind than do narrower shelters. A cane pushed into the ground on the opposite side to the stake will help prevent the shelter spinning round in the wind.

Shelterguards

These are a cross between a shelter and a guard, and are made of plastic mesh laminated with polythene film. The film degrades after two to three years, leaving the mesh to give longer term protection to the stem. Various sizes are available for trees and shrubs.

Plastic spiral guards

These prevent rabbits and voles stripping the bark from young trees, and are suitable for protecting the lower stem of large transplants which are at least 15cm (6") taller than the guard. Small transplants hidden within an opaque guard will not grow properly. Spiral guards can also be fitted to young established trees with a stem diameter of about 38mm (1.5"), to protect the bark after a treeshelter has been removed or disintegrated. Spiral guards can be re-used.

Spiral guards are available in brown, green, white and clear, and are supplied nested together for ease of transport. Depending on the size and type of planting stock, canes are normally needed to support the guard, otherwise the stem bends over under the weight of the guard. Spiral guards are not suitable for feathered trees, multi-stemmed shrubs or conifers, as they are only suitable for protecting a single, clear stem. Spiral guards are often used in addition to further protection, such as a perimeter fence to keep people and domestic stock at bay.

To fit, it's usually easier to fit the guard around the stem first, and then push the cane down through the guard and into the ground. Push the base of the guard a little way into the soil, to prevent it being dislodged by the wind or by animals. Once the stem has grown larger than about 5cm (2") diameter, gaps are created in the spiral and the guard no longer gives complete protection. Some guards disintegrate after a few years, whereas in more sheltered positions they can last almost indefinitely. Remove them once they become ineffective. Check particularly that the base of the guard is completely removed, and is not entangled at the base of the stem.

Vole and strimmer guards

These are short plastic guards which can be wrapped around the base of established young trees in areas where long grass can lead to explosions of vole populations. In most situations, treeshelters or spiral guards will give similar protection from the time of planting, but vole guards can be useful after shelters have been removed. Strimmer guards are used in mown areas to protect the stems of young trees, of over 6cm (2.5") stem diameter, from damage by strimmers and mowers. Some companies market the same product against voles and strimmers, others have separate products.

Plastic mesh guards

These are available in different sizes, heights and weights to protect against the full range of domestic and wild animals. They also protect against mower damage and inadvertent trampling, but are not vandal-proof. They give limited protection from wind damage. Mesh guards are recommended in preference to treeshelters for beech, as the humid atmosphere in treeshelters encourages the beech woolly aphid. Mesh guards need supporting by one or two stakes. On established trees, they can be used without stakes to prevent bark-stripping.

Various mesh sizes, colours and heights are available, either in rolls, or pre-cut and supplied as split tubes. Ring guns are available from tree guard suppliers, for quick fastening of rings to join mesh. Alternatively use tree shelter ties, or thread a bamboo cane through to join the ends of the mesh together.

Steel mesh guards

These are not generally used when planting transplants or other young trees, but are more suited to protecting the trunks of standard trees against vandalism, mowing or bark-stripping. They are more durable than plastic mesh, but are also more expensive. On some sites it may be worth substituting treeshelters or plastic mesh guards with steel mesh guards once the new trees are established, to give long term protection.

Mild steel guards and grilles

These may be needed to protect trees planted in pedestrian precincts, car-parks and other vulnerable sites. The grille prevents the tree being dug up, and protects the roots from surface damage.

Timber guards

Custom-built timber guards are suitable for long-term protection of individual trees in pastures and parkland. These can be designed to protect against domestic stock, as well as preventing mower damage and discouraging vandalism. They should be carefully designed and built, and constructed of preserved timber for durability. They are only worth doing well. A poorly constructed guard or one of weak timber will soon be damaged by stock.

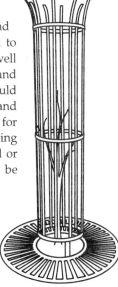

Within the timber surround, the young tree can be protected from voles, rabbits and hares by a treeshelter or spiral guard.

Tables 6e and 6f give information on suitable dimensions of fencing or timber guards to protect trees against different types of wild and domestic animals.

Table 6e: Spacing of verticals and horizontals

	Vertical and horizontal spacing (mm)	Horizontal spacing (mm)
	Zone A	Zone B
horses	100	500
cattle	100	500
deer	75	225
goats	75	225
sheep	50	150
hares	30	30
rabbits	30	30

Note the following:

• Make sure that all likely damaging animals are taken into account, as it is difficult to subsequently upgrade the protection.

• Unless vandalism is a problem, a section of climbable fence is useful for tending the tree.

• As with all young trees, keep a weed-free circle of at least 1m radius around the tree, by using a mulch or herbicide. If the entire enclosed area can be kept weed-free, this has the added benefit of removing the inducement for animals to lean over or push through to graze.

• It is not possible to build a tree guard simply of three or four posts with strained wire or netting, as sufficient strain to keep the wires taut will pull the posts inwards. Horizontal rails, preferably rebated, must be included (see below).

• Where netting is fitted to a surround, it's not usually a good idea to slant the posts outward to increase the distance of the top rail from the tree, as it's then difficult to fit the netting neatly.

• Barbed wire should not be automatically added, as this won't stop stock leaning over the barrier, but will make it difficult to climb in to tend the tree.

• The vulnerability to browsing or bark damage depends partly on the availability of other food, and the palatability of the planted trees. Where grass is plentiful,

Table 6f: Height of guard required (in metres)

Zone A   Zone B ▓▓▓▓

Distance from tree (in metres)	0-0.25	0.25-0.5	0.5-0.75	0.75-1.0	1.0-1.25	1.25-1.5	1.5-1.75	1.75-2.0	2.0-2.25	
horses	2.50	2.25	2.0	1.75	1.50	1.15	1.15	1.15	1.15	h
cattle	1.85	1.70	1.50	1.15	1.15	1.15	1.15	1.15	1.15	e
humans	2.25	1.90	1.70	1.50	1.35	1.15	1.15	1.15	1.15	i
red deer	2.10	175	1.45	1.20	1.20	1.20	1.20	1.50	1.80	g
fallow deer	1.80	1.60	1.25	1.10	1.10	1.10	1.35	180	1.80	h
goats	1.85	1.70	1.35	1.20	1.15	1.15	1.15	1.15	1.15	t
roe deer	1.60	1.35	1.10	1.0	1.0	1.0	1.60	1.80	1.80	
sheep	1.10	0.90	0.90	0.90	0.90	0.90	0.90	0.90	0.90	
hares	0.85	0.85	0.85	0.85	0.85	0.85	0.85	0.85	0.85	
rabbits	0.75	0.85	0.85	0.85	0.85	0.85	0.85	0.85	0.85	

trees may be ignored, although beech in particular tends to be targeted. It's vital to protect the leading shoot from any damage. Once this is out of reach, light browsing by cattle may not be a problem, and may merely encourage upward growth by 'side pruning'. Horses can be very destructive, particularly when they are bored, and can destroy a tree by bark-stripping.

The designs shown can be adapted using tables 6e and 6f. Unless using home-produced posts and rails, it's easier to design the surround using standard sizes of fencing materials. For example, standard 3.6m rails, cut into lengths as necessary, are used in the designs below.

The first design is proof against sheep, and against cattle in most situations.

The tall surround with rabbit netting around the lower section is proof against all likely damaging animals, except voles and squirrels. Attach one end of the upper netting by twisting the wires, without stapling. This allows the section of netting to be rolled back to give access for tending the tree. A heavy-duty mulch mat which covers the enclosed ground area is recommended for weed control inside netting surrounds, as accurate herbicide application may be difficult. This type of surround, which excludes browsing animals by height, rather than by reach, tends to be the most economical design. Its cage-like appearance can look rather unattractive.

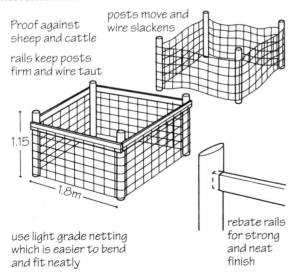

Proof against sheep and cattle

rails keep posts firm and wire taut

posts move and wire slackens

1.15

1.8m

use light grade netting which is easier to bend and fit neatly

rebate rails for strong and neat finish

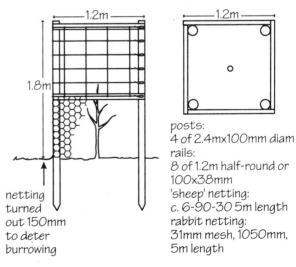

Proof against all animals listed in table 6f

1.2m

1.8m

1.2m

netting turned out 150mm to deter burrowing

posts:
4 of 2.4m x 100mm diam
rails:
8 of 1.2m half-round or 100x38mm
'sheep' netting:
c. 6-90-30 5m length
rabbit netting:
31mm mesh, 1050mm, 5m length

This type of fencing surround against horses and cattle is expensive in materials, but may be preferred because of its appearance. Sheep netting can be added, and individual rabbit guards used as necessary.

Proof against cattle and horses

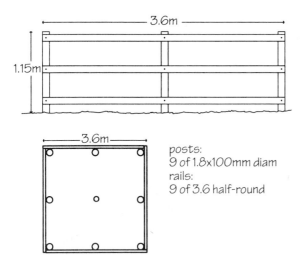

posts:
9 of 1.8x100mm diam
rails:
9 of 3.6 half-round

Planting a single tree in a surround is not necessarily the best way of creating a future specimen tree. The young tree will have a hostile microclimate with little shelter and low humidity, and even an expensive surround will not guarantee its survival. Where space is available, it may be better to plant a group of trees and shrubs, and then thin at a fairly early stage to leave the desired number of individual trees. Don't leave the thinning too late, or the trees will not have put out sufficient bracing roots, nor have the desired spreading shape for 'parkland' trees.

OTHER METHODS OF PROTECTING TREES

Thickets

Thickets of bramble, blackthorn and other prickly shrubs can be useful for hiding young trees from vandals, deer, and other unwanted attention. A shrub border will also give shelter from the wind and greatly increase the wildlife value of the planting. However, shrubs can also provide cover for vandals and deer, and need to be impenetrable to be totally effective. Brambles and blackthorn are very invasive, so regular management is needed to make sure they don't overtake the young trees.

Chemical repellents

Chemical repellents against deer have been tried in the past. These have included specially developed products, as well as wood preservatives and lion dung.

Chemical repellents may be useful for short term protection, for example if pest populations increase unexpectedly. Proprietary products, for example 'Aaprotect' are applied by spraying or painting vulnerable parts of the young tree,

and are mainly used for commercial conifer plantations. 'Aaprotect' can also be effective against rabbits. For further information see Pepper, Neil and Hemmings (1996).

Rags dipped in creosote have been used to deter deer. Tie the rags at deer head height at hedge gaps or points where deer enter the planting area. Brightly coloured plastic strips, old CDs and other waste materials have also been tried, but will only have short term effect, if any. The Forestry Commission tested the use of lion dung, but reported no measurable effect!

Post-planting care

The main priority in caring for all young trees in the first three years after planting is weed control, which is described in the following chapter. Watering is not usually practical in anything other than a garden situation. Fertilising is normally not necessary.

WEED CONTROL

The method of weed control should be decided upon at the earliest stage in planning planting, as it may affect the method of protection, spacing and other factors.

Herbicides are the most cost-effective method. Herbicides are applied either to bare ground in the winter, or to growing vegetation in spring.

Sheet or granular mulches can be spread immediately after planting, or during the first winter at any time before weed growth starts.

For full details on weed control see chapter 7.

PRUNING AT PLANTING

Good quality young trees, grown in a nursery, should have a balanced root to shoot ratio, making it unnecessary to prune at planting. Transplanted wild trees, or those which have been grown other than in a nursery may have too much top growth in relation to the root growth, and may have crossing branches or excess side branches. Leave the leader, but cut back side branches by at least one third, and remove any crossing branches which may rub. Very badly formed young trees, or those that are damaged, can be cut back to a stump of about 5cm (2"), which stimulates a new leader to grow.

Hard pruning or 'stumping back' can be a useful technique for hedging plants, notably hawthorn, or for planting in very vandal-prone areas. The stumps are barely visible in the first winter, and are fairly damage proof. By the time there is a noticeable amount of top growth, the young tree

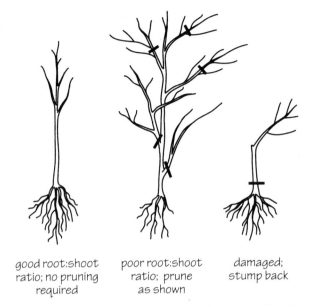

good root:shoot   poor root:shoot   damaged;
ratio; no pruning   ratio; prune   stump back
   required   as shown

should have put out a good amount of root growth and will be difficult to uproot by hand.

See chapter 7 for more information on pruning.

FIRMING UP

When weeding in early spring, and at other times as possible in the first year, check that the trees are still firm in the ground. Wind-sway can create a hollow around the root collar of the young tree, leaving it poorly supported. Frost action or moles can disturb the ground, loosening the roots. Tread around any loose stems to firm them into the ground. Check for any loose treeshelters or other tree protection, and tighten ties or replace stakes as necessary. Check particularly those young trees in exposed positions.

Natural colonisation and regeneration

Natural colonisation is the process by which trees and woodlands establish on sites which were previously unwooded. Natural regeneration is the process by which existing woodlands regenerate. In practice, the distinction is blurred where there are scattered trees in wood pastures, commons, heaths and other areas.

Natural regeneration has several advantages in woodland creation:

- The species will be matched to the site, and local genetic stock will be conserved.

- A natural, uneven distribution will result, with structural diversity.

- There are no costs in purchasing or planting trees, but fencing or other protection may be needed.

Natural regeneration is supported by the Woodland Grant Scheme, both for restocking areas in existing woodlands, and for creating new woodlands by extending from an existing woodland. Where natural regeneration is practical and appropriate, grant aid for planting will not normally be granted. Between 1992-97 about 15% of approved new planting was through natural regeneration, the majority of it in Scotland.

Natural regeneration requires:

- A good source of seed nearby. Trees do not produce seed every year, and seed of most species does not remain viable for many years. Most species germinate in the year following production.

- Sparse ground vegetation. Seeds will not germinate easily in thick grass, bramble or other dense ground vegetation, and seedlings will be suppressed by such growth. For this reason, natural colonisation by trees is often associated with poor stony substrates, sandy soils and other sites where grass and other dense ground vegetation cannot survive.

- Protection from animals and people. Squirrels, mice and voles may eat seed before it has germinated. Rabbits, deer and stock may browse on the newly germinated trees. Heavy use by people will trample and destroy seedling trees.

Some tree species, which are called colonisers, produce seed more frequently and abundantly than other species. The seed is usually light in weight, so it can be dispersed easily by the wind, and the trees tolerate a wide range of soil conditions. Examples are beech, willow, pine and sycamore. Heavy seeds and fruits of other species may be taken by birds or animals, and dispersed some distance, but distribution will only be patchy.

Table 6g (overleaf) indicates the seed characteristics of native trees (based on Harmer, 1999).

Natural colonisation as a way of creating a new woodland can be very successful in particular locations, such as urban fringe land, abandoned industrial sites and other areas where soils are poor and there are good seed sources nearby. Such woodland is less of a target for vandalism than are newly planted trees.

If a particular site for woodland creation already has evidence of natural regeneration, this can be allowed to develop. Fencing or individual protection of trees may be necessary, depending on the likelihood of damage from animals or people. In vandal prone areas, fencing or individual protection can be counter productive.

Where regeneration is very dense, treeshelters or spiral guards can be used as a way of thinning or 'respacing' the seedling trees. Seedling trees can be protected at the desired

Table 6g: Seed characteristics of native trees

SPECIES	DISTANCE (m)	MODE	FREQUENCY (years)
Oak	20	G, M, B	3-5+
Ash	50-100	W	1-3
Birch	100-200	W	1-2
Cherry	-	G, M, B	1-3
Alder	20	W	1-3
Beech	20	G, M	5-15
Sycamore	50-100	W	1-2
Rowan	-	G, B	1-2
Sweet chestnut	20	G, M	1-4
Willows	100-200	W	1-2
Field maple	50-100	W	2
Hazel	20	G, M	2-3
Aspen	100-200	W	1-2
Lime, small leaved	50-100	W	2-3
Hornbeam	50-100	W, M	2-4
Whitebeam	-	G, B	2-3
Crab apple	20	G, M	1-2
Bird cherry	-	G, B	1-2
Elm, wych	50-100	W	2
Yew	-	G, B	1-2
Scot's pine	100-200	W	2-3
Wild service tree	-	G, B	1-2
Holly	-	G, B	2-4

Distance = maximum distance at which colonisation can be reasonably expected to occur. No figure is given for seed dispersed by birds.

Mode = method of dispersal. G-gravity, W-wind, B-bird, M-mammal

Frequency = interval between good seed years

spacing, for example 2m apart, with the others left to be browsed or trampled. Seedlings of other species can be planted at the same time, to grow up together with the natural regeneration. This can be easier to manage than trying to introduce them at a later stage, when some thinning of the canopy may be necessary.

More usually, colonisation of new sites will tend to spread slowly from the edges, or in the vicinity of a particular tree, so the development of a new woodland will be gradual and patchy. This is not necessarily a problem, as the range of habitats produced will have high wildlife value.

Natural regeneration as a way of restocking existing woodlands is not an easy process. As well as the factors listed above, it requires sufficient space and sunlight in the canopy to permit regeneration and good early growth, but not so much sunlight that weed growth becomes prolific.

GROUND PREPARATION

Provided the conditions listed above are fulfilled, germination can be encouraged by preparing the ground in the vicinity of the seeding trees. The area should be cleared of grass and other ground vegetation, by hand weeding or use of herbicide. Ash and beech in particular require weed-free ground for germination, while oak can germinate through a grass sward or other growth. Raking the ground can help provide a good surface for germination.

Viable beech seed is only produced on average about every 10 years, in a year following a long, hot summer which stimulates the production of flower buds. Beech leaf litter is very slow to break down, and if the seeds fall onto deep litter they find it difficult to root through to the mineral layer below. In a beech 'mast' year, you can encourage germination by raking the seed-covered ground, to mix the litter and mineral layer and trample the seed into the soil, where it will also be protected from squirrels. On the continent of Europe this mixing and trampling is done by wild boar, and in the past in Britain was probably done by boar and domestic swine. This action can also be imitated by dragging logs across the ground, or by shallow rotavating, but care must be taken not to damage surface roots or compact the ground.

Tree seeds germinate best on soil which is well drained at the surface, with plenty of leaf mould or mulch to suppress other growth. Ground that has become compacted through trampling or machine use and is wet at the surface will not result in good germination.

The soil in newly-cleared areas of woodland often 're-wets', due to the sudden reduction in transpiration when trees are removed, and to disturbance of the soil structure through felling operations. It's best to get tree cover established again as soon as possible, as otherwise such areas get rapidly overgrown with rushes and tussocky grasses, making regeneration or planting difficult. It may be possible to dig temporary drainage ditches to improve surface conditions and allow regeneration to take place. Cultivation is unlikely to help in soils which are already wet. If natural regeneration is unsuccessful, planting should be carried out the next season, choosing planting positions on any drier mounds or ridges on the site.

PROTECTION AND EARLY CARE

Techniques for protecting naturally regenerated seedlings are the same as for planted seedlings (p82). However, the need is likely to be greater, because regeneration necessarily occurs near or within existing woodland, which will provide cover and shelter for the animals which damage young trees. Natural seedlings appear to be less palatable to deer than planted trees are, possibly because transplants retain higher nitrate content from nursery applications of nitrogen, which make them more inviting to eat.

Deer have become a serious problem in many woodlands, and will affect the success of regeneration, and also the regrowth of coppice, which may be cut as part of a woodland

management programme. Electric fencing can be used around woodland regeneration plots and newly-cut coppice coupes, to deter deer. Dead hedges of woven coppice material or brashings can also be successful.

Dead hedges have the advantage of using locally available material, and tend to result in fewer negative comments from visitors than does the presence of electric fencing. It's possible for a pair of volunteers to erect about 20m (22 yards) of 2m (6ft) high dead hedging in a day, so the technique is a viable one for small regeneration plots.

Erect stakes about 2m (6') high, using the stoutest coppice stems available. Push them into the ground, first using a crowbar to make a hole as necessary. Then roughly weave the cut material between the stakes, treading on it as you go to pack it down tightly. The result should be a dense barrier about 1m (3') wide and 2m (6') high, with no gaps visible through it. The dead hedges eventually rot down, benefiting the woodland ecosystem, and avoiding any removal costs.

Dead hedge - half completed

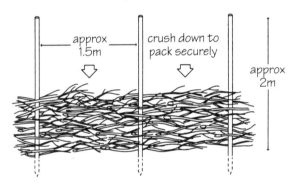

Treeshelters are normally the best method for protecting seedlings, and provide a useful marker for weeding operations. Weeding must be continued for at least three years, until the leading shoots of the trees are well clear of competing weeds. As a rule of thumb, trees should be at least 1.8m (6') high and growing well. Bramble can be a problem as it can clamber higher, but will not adversely affect strongly growing trees. Eventually the bramble will be suppressed, but sometimes it may be preferable to clear it, or cut the stems to prevent it spreading, at the stage before the canopy closes.

Sometimes natural regeneration is so successful that a dense sward of seedling trees results. These can be thinned by cutting swathes through with a scythe or brush cutter while the trees are still tiny. Seedlings can also be transplanted within the site. They tend to grow away well as they are of an appropriate strain, and have the right mycorrhizal association in place.

If thick stands of regeneration are left to grow up to sapling stage they must be thinned. For more information on thinning see page 110.

7   Aftercare

Aftercare, and in particular weeding, is vital to the survival of newly planted trees. In the past many planting schemes have failed due to lack of care in the years immediately after planting. These first three or so years are vitally important. Fast growth means that the tree is vulnerable to vandals and other damaging agents for the shortest possible time. If the trees make good roots and sturdy top growth during these first years they will be able to withstand drought, be resistant to disease, and leaders will grow beyond the reach of browsing animals. If closely planted, the trees will rapidly form a closed canopy. This in turn will suppress weed growth, and the trees will mutually benefit each other so that a young woodland will quickly establish.

If aftercare is lacking, the young trees will malinger for a few years, putting on little new growth, or dying back and then trying to regrow from the stem. In mown grass such trees can hang around for many years without making any significant growth, creating an eyesore and a hindrance to other uses of the space. Unweeded young trees in long grass will be lost from view within a season, and many may die.

This chapter covers weeding techniques, control of woody weeds, the management of glades and paths, and the introduction of woodland flora. Information is also given on pruning, and control of pests and diseases. Felling techniques for early thinning of woodlands are outlined, as are coppicing and pollarding of young trees.

Weeding

Newly planted trees require a weed-free area of at least one metre diameter around the stem, for at least three years after planting. This area can be kept weed-free by herbicides or mulches. Hoeing or other hand weeding can also be used, but is much more labour-intensive.

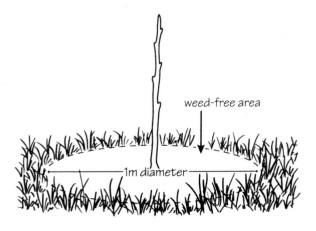

weed-free area

1m diameter

The frequency of weeding and the type of control used will depend on the situation, soil fertility and other factors. The weed problem will be worse where soils are fertile, or where there is a large bank of weed seeds in the ground or spreading from nearby. Weeds, and especially grass, will grow more prolifically in unshaded sites. Young trees planted in woodland clearings will need to be kept free of brambles, nettles and herbaceous growth, but in general weeding will be less of a problem than in open situations.

Fertile, open sites, and particularly pastures, arable fields and other farmland will have high fertility and may have a large seed bank, and are likely to require the most frequent weeding and for the longest number of years.

HOW WEEDS COMPETE

Weeds, especially grasses and clovers, compete strongly with young trees for water, light and nutrients.

At the early stage of growth, young trees rely on moisture in the soil's surface layer. If weeds are allowed to grow up around the base of a tree, they will compete strongly for this water by drawing it up and transpiring it through their leaves. During dry weather, weeds continue to draw up moisture from deeper in the soil. An unweeded tree avoids the moisture stress caused by this competition by reducing its area of foliage, for example by producing smaller leaves. This reduces the tree's capacity to photosynthesise, which in turns slows root growth. As root growth is needed for the uptake of water, the unweeded tree will be caught in a vicious circle, and will die back or fail.

On an area of bare soil, the rate of water lost through evaporation will be much lower, and the tree will be much less stressed. Evaporation will slow further during dry weather, when a skin of dry soil forms at the surface. An exception are clay soils, which crack and dry out during drought. A thick covering of mulch will reduce cracking and help retain moisture.

Nutrients are only available to the tree through the mechanism of water uptake. Thus, a tree which appears to be suffering from a nutrient deficiency in the soil, may actually be suffering from competing weeds taking up most of the available water and nutrients. Where fertiliser is applied to young trees, it's even more important to keep a weed-free zone, otherwise the extra nutrients will merely stimulate the growth of weeds, at the expense of the planted trees.

Benefits of weed-free area

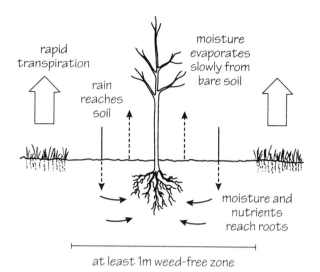

rapid transpiration

rain reaches soil

moisture evaporates slowly from bare soil

moisture and nutrients reach roots

at least 1m weed-free zone

TIMING AND DURATION

Competition from weeds is usually at its strongest in April, May and June. April is also the month in which soil moisture deficits begin to develop over much of England, and the transpiration from weeds from this time will result in even greater deficits for the entire growing season. Thus, even one week's weed growth in April can significantly reduce water availability right through to October.

Timing will vary with the method of control, the locality and the season. Sheet mulches (p99) are fitted at the time of planting and left in position until they deteriorate. Herbicide application must be carefully timed according to the type of herbicide, the amount of growth, and the weather. Translocated herbicides can only be applied to weeds in growth, but the aim should be to have bare ground around the tree for the maximum length of time throughout the year. Grass, the greatest enemy to tree growth, can grow at any time of year, provided the weather is mild. Tree roots also grow in mild spells in winter, even when they are not in leaf. Bare ground is therefore important even in the winter. A young tree that puts on root growth through the winter will show significantly better leaf and stem growth in the following season than one which has not.

If the early season weeding is thorough, the trees may be able to withstand some weed competition later on in the season, but they will grow best if kept weed-free throughout the year.

The number of years that weed control is needed depends on the site, the species planted, the spacing of the trees and other factors. Three years from the time of planting is usually the minimum. Single trees in open ground and trees at the edges of planted areas need weeding for a longer period than trees within woodlands, where the relative lack of light does not encourage the growth of grasses. Trees in grassland should have a weed-free surround for at least five years. The ground under trees cropped for fruit in orchards and gardens should be kept permanently bare.

HERBICIDES

The Control of Pesticides Regulations 1986 covers all aspects of the development, sale, supply, storage and use of herbicides.

The regulations cover proprietary products rather than active ingredients, and classify these products according to approved use. 'Professional' products are formulated for use in agriculture, horticulture and forestry, and 'amateur' products are formulated for use in the garden. Amateur products may contain the same active ingredients as those in the professional category, but at lower strengths, so there is less dilution required before application.

Regular mowing or strimming around the base of trees is not a method of weed control, as repeated cutting simply stimulates grass growth, and makes moisture and nutrient deficiencies even worse. Mown grass is therefore more damaging than long grass, and causes further problems, as damage to the bark from mowers or strimmers is almost inevitable. As well as the physical damage to the stem, disease often enters through damaged bark. Mown grass is the worst way of managing the ground around newly planted trees.

Mown grass can also compete with older trees. Trees that have been growing for many years in grassland and which are not thriving can sometimes be encouraged into growth by killing off the surrounding grass.

In some situations weed control does not have to be total. Too heavy a weeding of woody and herbaceous growth should be avoided, as these weeds do not compete so strongly for water and nutrients, and their removal is likely to encourage grasses to establish instead. In some cases, tall, sparse weeds such as bramble and nettles can be beneficial, as they protect trees from drying winds and damage from deer, hares or vandals. Periodic checks are needed to make sure they are not interfering with tree growth. Some plants collapse as they die back in autumn, and need clearing before they smother the young trees.

Bracken should be controlled, as it competes strongly with young trees for light in the early part of the growing season, and then collapses, often smothering young trees. Goose grass, an annual, can also smother young trees in a season. Old man's beard must also be controlled.

Bluebells and other low herbaceous woodland flora can be left, as they do not harm trees. Mosses, which have no roots, do not appreciably lower the soil's water content and may help to stabilise and protect the soil around the tree by forming a natural 'mulch'.

From the range permitted for amateur use, there are two products which are widely available from garden centres and tree growers, and which are suitable for use on small-scale tree planting schemes. For large schemes, or for groups undertaking regular tree planting, training in the use of professional products is advisable, as these are more cost-effective than the equivalent amateur products.

When using herbicides, whether professional or amateur, follow the instructions on the label. Note the recommended dosage and the required weather conditions for effective use. Clothing and equipment should be correct and appropriate, as identified by the assessment of the chemical's use.

Propyzamide (Kerb Granules) is a residual and foliar acting herbicide, although it is more effective as the former. It can be applied to bare ground to prevent weeds germinating, or it can be applied to weeds in growth and is translocated to kill the roots. It remains active for at least 12 weeks. As a residual herbicide, results are best if it is applied to soil with a firm, fine tilth. If applied to very lumpy soil, as the lumps crumble untreated soil will be exposed and weed growth will result. Rain is needed after application to move residual herbicide into the soil. Kerb Granules are available in a 120 tree 'shaker pack' (£10.50 at 2000 prices), or in larger quantities.

Glyphosate (eg Roundup Biactive 120g/l) is a widely used garden herbicide, which is applied by spray to the leaves. It is translocated through the plant, killing all of it above and below ground, and is effective on all grasses and herbaceous growth. It is inactivated and biodegrades on contact with the ground. Contact with tree foliage, shoots and bark must be avoided, or tree growth will be damaged. Glyphosate can be used at any time when vegetation is actively growing. Depending on weed growth, glyphosate should be applied in March/April, and again in August to benefit late summer tree growth. It costs about 5p per tree per application (2000 prices), and can be applied using a garden sprayer of one litre capacity or greater.

The combination of using a winter pre-emergent/residual herbicide and a translocated/foliar acting herbicide in spring and summer is widely used for tree planting schemes. The foliar acting herbicide can be used as the residual product wears off, and also on any weeds which are resistant to the residual product. This creates bare ground, to which the residual herbicide can be applied again to delay reinvasion. Using a translocated herbicide does have the disadvantage that it can only be applied to growing weeds, so by the time it is applied, there has already been some interference with tree growth. However, herbicides are the most cost-effective method of weed control for tree planting schemes, and are preferred over mulches by most authorities responsible for tree planting.

The sale and use of professional herbicides is strictly regulated. Products can only be sold to and used by holders of the National Proficiency Training Council (NPTC) Certificate of Competence. Professional products are only available from specialist suppliers, whose staff must also be certificate holders in order to advise on herbicide use.

Training leading to the NPTC Certificate of Competence is provided at agricultural colleges and other centres throughout the United Kingdom. Enquire through the NPTC, the Forestry and Arboricultural Safety and Training Council, or Lantra (formerly the Agricultural Training Board). For contact addresses see pages 114-115.

Information on herbicides for professional use in forestry and farm woodlands is given in *The use of Herbicides in the Forest* (Forestry Commission, 1995) and *Herbicides for Farm Woodlands and Short Rotation Coppice* (Forestry Commission, 1996).

MULCHES

Mulches are materials which are put down on the ground to suppress weeds and keep moisture in the ground by reducing evaporation. They can either be sheet materials, such as polythene, bitumen or various textiles, or loose materials such as bark, chipped wood or gravel.

Proprietary sheet mulches

Sheet mulch materials or mulch mats have the dual advantage of suppressing weeds, and reducing or preventing evaporation from the soil surface. They also increase soil temperature, which encourages root growth in early spring. Sheet mulches which prevent evaporation are not recommended for badly drained sites, as this will exacerbate waterlogging and encourage anaerobic conditions.

Proprietary sheet mulches are quite expensive, but it is not usually worth economising by using cheaper products or recycled waste materials. Sheet mulches need to be substantial enough to last at least three years, thick enough to resist damage, and large enough to be effective. The sheet mulch tends to invigorate the growth of grasses around its edge, so a mat smaller than 50cm square will be ineffective. The larger size mats, 1m square, are recommended.

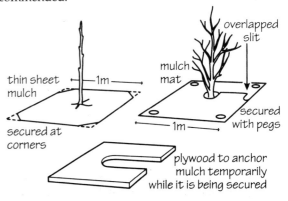

Table 7a: Comparison of mulch mats and herbicides

MULCH MATS	HERBICIDES
Only needs doing once, provided a durable product is used	Repeat applications necessary
Can be fitted by volunteers	Trained staff needed for professional products
Can be damaged by animals or vandals	Cannot be damaged
No adverse effects on trees	Can damage trees if wrongly applied
Fitting not weather dependent	Application weather dependent
High initial cost	Repeat lower costs
May encourage voles	Discourages voles

Mulch mats can be anchored into the soil at the edges or corners, or fastened by proprietary pegs. Suppliers will recommend the best method for particular products. Pegs add to the cost of the product, with the 1m square mats requiring nine pegs per mat. Non-biodegradable mats should be further weighted down by stones, gravel, upturned turves or a small amount of soil, to weight the mulch and discourage animals from disturbing it. Don't use too thick a layer of soil or weeds will establish in it. Biodegradable mats should be anchored by pegs or stones, and not by covering with soil, as this makes the material degrade more quickly.

Weeds can grow up through the gap around the stem, or along the slit which allows the mat to be fitted around the tree. Some products have an overlap to prevent this weed growth occurring.

Mulch mats are not foolproof. Mats can be disturbed by vandals, or torn by the wind, and may need replacing during the initial three year weeding period. Thinner materials can be scratched and torn by animals, especially if voles take up residence beneath the mat, as foxes will then tear the mats to reach the voles. Some fibrous mats may be damaged by large birds in search of nesting material.

A wide range of sheet mulches are available from Acorn Planting Products and Greentech (p119). Woven polypropylene is probably the best compromise for price versus quality for most projects, but situations differ, and new products may become available. Some products use recycled materials, including wool.

DIY recycled materials

Probably the best recycled product is disused carpet, provided it is made of natural, biodegradable material, rather than nylon or acrylic. It's long-lasting, heavy enough to stay in place without weighting, is relatively tidy and unobtrusive, and is air and water permeable. Old carpet should be readily obtainable from carpet fitters. Disused books of samples are ready cut in squares, and only need slitting to fit. Lay with the underside up.

Old lino or other flooring materials are also suitable, as is roofing felt. Thick black plastic, as used for covering silage clamps on farms or for other wrapping purposes may be salvageable. Large sheets of black plastic can be laid down and the trees slit planted through them. Sideways water movement through the soil is sufficient to keep the trees watered, although voles may be a problem. The plastic looks unsightly, but can result in very rapid tree growth and leaves the ground clear for establishing woodland flora.

With all recycled materials, make sure that they are safe to handle, and do not contain residues that may either harm the people laying the material, or contaminate the ground.

Loose mulch materials

Loose mulch materials such as composted bark are commonly used in parks and gardens, both for new plantings, and as general soil improvers. As the material breaks down it is incorporated into the soil, adding to the organic matter content, improving soil structure and helping to maintain nutrient levels. However, a layer at least 10cm (4") thick is needed to be effective, and this will only remain on the surface for about a year, before it becomes incorporated into the soil.

The mulch should cover an area at least 1m diameter. Keep it away from the stem, or rot may result. Mulch can be laid at the time of planting, or in very early spring, before growth starts again. Replace annually in winter.

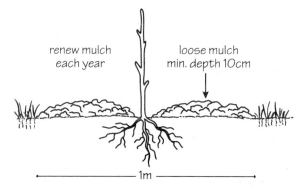

renew mulch each year

loose mulch min. depth 10cm

1m

For use in tree planting schemes, loose mulch materials are only worth considering when there is a supply of suitable material readily available. One of the best methods is to combine the need for mulching materials with disposal of prunings, thinnings and other woody material. Instead of being burnt, material can be put through a wood chipper, preferably composted for a few months, and then used for mulch. Many woodland management schemes use this method of recycling within their own area of woodland. Woody material is best composted before use, or it may deprive the trees of available nitrogen as it decomposes. In practice, it is often applied fresh, without apparent problems. If possible, compost it within existing woodland, or close to but not under the canopies of existing mature trees. This may encourage mycorrhizal activity which will enhance its use as a mulch (p70).

Decaying leaves, either gathered from existing woodland, or swept up from parks and gardens are excellent mulch material, and are beneficial in encouraging mycorrhizal activity.

Any woody material which can be brought into the young woodland will help the development of a woodland ecosystem. Logs and larger branches can be left in small piles, or scattered through the wood where they will not hinder access or weeding operations. They can be placed next to young trees, where they will suppress weeds and break down to form a mulch, or can be used to weigh down other mulching materials. Brashings or prunings can be used to deter deer, access and vandalism, although this needs to be weighed against the chance of attracting arson, as well as giving cover for rabbits. Brambles also tend to grow up through piles of brashings, which may or may not be helpful!

Spoiled hay, straw and other bulky materials are suitable as long as they are well rotted. Don't use silage, slurry or other farm wastes as these can be toxic to young trees and other plants.

Loose mulch is not totally effective in suppressing weeds, whether or not it is laid on bare ground. Some weeds will come up through the mulch, and others will seed into it. Goose grass for example can spread very quickly after germinating in loose mulch. Hand weeding will normally be needed twice or more during the growing season. If grasses get a hold, a herbicide is the best way of getting rid of them. Loose mulches should be replaced each winter for three or more years, until the young trees are established. Once the canopy starts to close, the young woodland produces its own mulch of fallen leaves.

HAND WEEDING

Hand weeding is labour intensive, and only suitable for small planting schemes. Hand-pull any weeds that come out easily, and avoid using tools. You should never use a fork or spade near a young tree, as it is easy to damage the roots or stem. A hoe can be used on weed seedlings, but take great care not to damage the stem of the tree. If hand weeding is to be used, it should be combined with using a mulch of leaf-mould or compost. This will keep down the growth of grasses, so you should only need to pull out those plants which seed into the mulch. Where grasses have taken a hold, it's generally best to use a contact herbicide to destroy the sward, and then try to keep the area weed free by mulching or hoeing.

Weak herbaceous growth such as nettles, creeping thistles and many tall annuals or biennials can be hand pulled, but make sure this doesn't then allow the growth of grasses, which will be much more damaging. Pulled material can be piled up around the trees to act as a mulch. Larger areas of nettles, thistles or bracken can be trampled, which suppresses rather than stimulates growth, but may need to be repeated a few times through the season. Bracken can also be 'whipped' with a stick as the fronds open, to weaken the growth, but beware of damaging the young trees.

Bracken can be a problem in old pasture woodlands and parks. One of the best control methods is to trample or roll the growth in July, which flattens and bruises the stems, but does not sever them. This encourages water loss from the plant, and prevents re-supply of nutrients to next year's dormant buds. Various commercial rollers are available which can be towed by small tractors and four-wheel drive vehicles (*Enact* Vol 5 No 3). Bracken can be a serious fire risk where there is a deep accumulation of litter, which should be raked away from tree planting sites.

INTER-ROW WEEDING

The 1m radius circle around each tree must be kept weed free. Where trees are planted at 2m spacing, this will result in the whole area being kept weed-free, which is the best option for successful tree establishment. Where spacing is 3m or more, the remaining area between the trees, which may or may not be in rows, can be left to grow up, or can be mown.

Leaving the inter-row vegetation to grow up unmanaged is useful for hiding the trees from vandals, and for discouraging people from crossing the site and inadvertently damaging the young trees. On windy, exposed sites inter-row growth also helps shelter the young trees from the wind. However, you need to check that growth does not get so tall that when it collapses in late summer, it crushes the young trees. This can be a particular problem is there is a wet spell of weather in late summer. Voles can be a problem in tall grass, so vole guards (p83) may be needed. Depending on the site, inter-row growth can include plants which add to the wildlife value, and which are not damaging to tree growth. These may include arable weeds or common woodland edge plants. If there is anything particularly special, you are probably planting on the wrong site!

Where neatness is important, and vandalism unlikely, mowing is an option. It prevents bramble, thistles or other troublesome weeds establishing, and also removes the cover for voles. Take great care when mowing, brush cutting or strimming, and never be tempted to cut near the tree stems, even if there is weed growth there, as damage to the stem is inevitable.

Long handled scythes are not recommended for weeding amongst young trees, as it is far too easy to damage or sever the trees. Short-handled sickles or grass hooks may be useful in some circumstances, but again great care is needed. Treeshelters or other protection make it easier to see and avoid the young trees, but shelters and the trees within them are not proof against damage from an edged tool.

Controlling woody weeds

Woody weeds are less harmful than grasses to the growth of young trees. A continuous cover of vigorous woody shrubs will, however, compete strongly with young trees if the soil is very poor, as water and nutrients will be in short supply.

In woodland planting schemes where the primary aim is conservation and amenity, any native shrubs and trees which colonise the planted area are usually desirable, as they provide greater variety of species, structure and cover. It may be necessary, however, to control them for several reasons. These include keeping glades and rides open, allowing the more desirable trees to thrive, maintaining a full range of woodland structure, and allowing access for management and recreation. Too dense regeneration will result in spindly, unstable trees, heavy shade and a poor ground flora.

Certain invasive introduced species such as sycamore and rhododendron, and invasive native species such as birch, willow, elder and wayfaring tree, may need controlling. Rhododendron can be a huge problem in woodlands on acid soils, as it propagates vigorously, both thrives in and casts heavy shade, and creates toxic conditions in the soil when its leaves rot and fall.

If you cut woody weeds by hand, you will normally need to remove the stump or treat it to prevent regrowth. You can remove the stump by hand or winch, or kill it with a herbicide. Where deer populations are high, you may find that by protecting the desired species against deer, the unwanted sycamore, birch or willow regrowth is heavily browsed, so reducing its competitiveness.

Saplings and other unwanted woody growth can be killed by ring-barking the stem. This will leave the dead growth

in position, which may be undesirable, looks unattractive and may be unsafe. On the other hand, the dead growth can be useful in screening and protecting the desirable species, and also continues to provide some cover for wildlife. Regrowth of the ring-barked plants from the base is also less vigorous than if the stem is severed. Ring-barking is simple to do on single-stemmed saplings, but awkward on multi-stemmed shrubs. Ring-barking which is not thorough can stimulate the plant to produce an unusually large crop of seed.

Another alternative for controlling scrub, is to cut it at the base and then lay the cut stems over the stools. This can be done with hawthorn, blackthorn, willow or sycamore to make an informal laid barrier or thicket, to protect and screen new plantings. This will also suppress the scrub growth for a few years, by which time the desirable trees should have grown sufficiently to shade out the unwanted species. The procedure of cutting and laying is very much quicker than cutting and removing or burning plus stump removal. However, the unkempt and tangled appearance of the developing woodland may make it unsuitable for sites with public access.

The control of one year old seedlings by pulling or herbicide application, and removal of seeding trees, can also be useful measures.

Techniques for cutting smaller trees and shrubs are covered at the end of this chapter.

HERBICIDES FOR WOODY WEEDS

Herbicides can be applied direct to the foliage of shrubs which are in leaf, but this is not suitable work for volunteer groups. For details of professional products see *The Use of Herbicides in the Forest* (Willoughby and Dewar, 1995).

Herbicides can also be applied to the cut stump to prevent regrowth. This can be a useful technique as it only affects the treated stump, and there is no unsightly dead material left standing. It is labour intensive, as clearance still has to be done, and the cut material removed, stacked or burned. Stump treatment avoids the ground disturbance caused by stump removal, although the cut stumps may be a hazard for walkers. Where machinery is to be used, for example to mow woodland glades or edges, the cut stumps must be below the operating clearance of the machine.

Ammonium sulphamate (Amcide or Root-out), is an amateur herbicide which can be applied to cut stumps. Glyphosate (Roundup tough weed killer) is also effective on cut stumps. Follow the manufacturer's instructions regarding application.

Beating up

This is a forestry term which refers to the replacement of newly planted trees which have died. Even with the best planting and management, a percentage of trees will not survive the first season. In commercial forestry where it's important to maximise timber production on a site, replacement is necessary. Grant conditions and contract agreements for planting schemes normally include a requirement for replacement of failed plants.

Replacement is also important for other woodland plantings where the aim is to produce a woodland with a closed canopy as soon as possible. If some fail, this will affect the conditions of shelter, humidity and shade, to the detriment of the whole scheme.

Beating up is best done in the first two years after planting, or the replacements will have little chance of catching up with the other trees. Where trees are spaced 3m (10') apart or wider, all the failed trees should be replaced. For 2m (6') spacing, it may be sufficient to replace one plant for every two failures, depending on the proportion that have failed.

If a high proportion of plants of the same species have failed, it's either because they don't suit the site, or because they were sub-standard on delivery. The supplier should be contacted for advice. Where failures occur in clusters or to a particular pattern on the site, the site conditions are probably the cause. Before you replant, check the area for poor drainage or other soil problems. If failure is due to vandalism or accidental trampling, protective measures may need to be taken.

Management of glades, rides and paths

A well managed system of rides and paths within the woodland is important for several reasons:

- Management of the developing woodland, including weeding and pruning, is much simpler if access is easy.

- Trampling and damage to the young trees is less likely if access routes are well planned and clearly defined. Attractive paths and edges, which are the visible parts of the woodland, also make the wood look well cared for, so it will hopefully be better respected.

- Attractive access routes will encourage people to walk in the wood and take an interest in its development.

- Glades and rides, and their edges where they merge to woodland, are important wildlife habitats (p22).

- In larger woods, gravel roads accessible to vehicles in any season are important for viable extraction of timber

and other products. These roads are best made before the woodland is planted.

In the early stages of woodland development, paths can be maintained as mown grass. The grassy edges can be left to grow longer, and will provide useful wildlife habitat. As the trees grow up and the canopy closes, grass will be shaded out. Depending on the type of ground and the

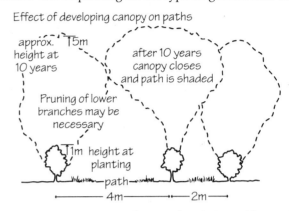

Effect of developing canopy on paths

amount of use, paths may then need surfacing with gravel or woodchips to make them pleasant for walking.

As the woodland develops, sections alongside the main paths may need to be kept clear of understorey, to lessen perceptions of danger. Cleared areas also open up views, are attractive for children's play, and bring sunlight to the woodland floor. As tree height increases, some felling may be required to maintain grassy glades and rides, which are valued for wildlife and recreation. Vary the edges of paths to diversify the habitat and to add interest to the view. (See diagram overleaf.)

For details on path design, construction and management, including the restriction of unwanted access, see *Footpaths* (BTCV, 1996). Details are also included on techniques suitable for building woodland roads, using hardcore and other recycled materials.

MANAGING GLADES AND RIDES

Most glades will develop from the existing grass sward into which the trees were planted. On sites which start as bare ground, glades can be sown with a mixture of grasses and wild flowers. Generally these mixes comprise about 20% native wild flowers and 80% grasses, with different mixes available for sunny or shady sites, different soil types, woodland edge, hedgerows, for early or late flowering and so on. A general mix which contains species with a fairly wide tolerance of conditions is likely to be the most successful.

Glades can be managed in a variety of ways, to manage or encourage different types of flowering plants and grasses. In established woodlands, grazing by rabbits or deer may keep grassy areas open, but in new woodlands, mowing will be necessary. Mowing regimes should be chosen to

PATHS AND GLADES IN MATURING WOODLAND

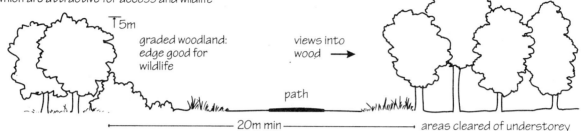

Space required for sunny, open areas
which are attractive for access and wildlife

graded woodland:
edge good for
wildlife

views into
wood ⟶

path

⟵ 20m min ⟶   areas cleared of understorey

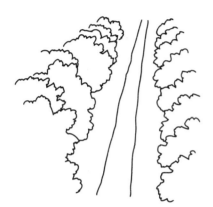

monotonous path edges

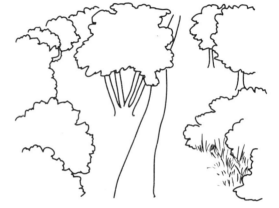

vary path edges to enhance habitats and views

encourage flowering and seeding of the chosen wildflower seed mix, or of plants already on the site. In general, mowings should be removed off the site to reduce nutrients and encourage diversity of plant species.

There are three basic regimes:

• Spring meadow. This contains a high proportion of plants which flower in spring. It should be cut as a traditional hay meadow, in May, after plants have set seed. Leave the cut material to dry in situ and drop its seed, and then gather it up. It can be used as hay, or composted and used as a mulch amongst the growing trees.

• Flowery lawn. Some flowering perennials are adapted to close-mown conditions and frequent trampling. If mowing is stopped or trampling is discouraged for a few weeks in May and early June, the plants have a chance to flower. This treatment is useful for areas which need to be kept reasonably short and tidy.

• Summer meadow. This includes species that flower in late summer and that are attractive to many butterflies. Cut regularly from April to June to discourage coarse grasses becoming dominant, and remove the cuttings.

For further details on management of glades and meadows see *The Urban Handbook* (BTCV, 1998) and *Wildflowers Work* (Landlife, 1994). Catalogues of wildflower suppliers also contain useful information on sowing and management.

Edges of glades should have a variety of taller perennials, shrubs and small trees to create shelter, both in the glade and the woodland, and as a wildlife habitat. Edges that face south or west and are open to the sun are particularly valuable for birds and insects. See page 24 for advice on edge management.

Woodland flora

The natural spread of woodland field layer plants will depend on various factors:

• Soil type. On agricultural soils which have been cultivated for many years there will be high fertility and a poor seed bank of native woodland plants. Growth of the less desirable plants such as nettles, docks, brambles and thistles is likely to be prolific.

• Proximity of other woodlands. If there are existing woods, copses or hedgerows adjacent to the new planting, there is a good chance of woodland plants spreading into the wood. Where possible, abut new planting to existing trees.

• Closure of the woodland canopy. Woodland plants cannot compete where there is sufficient light for grasses to grow. As the canopy closes and leaf litter builds up the conditions become suitable for woodland plants to grow.

- Size of the woodland area. A woodland smaller than about 40m x 40m, or a strip narrower than about 15m, will never create sufficient shade to allow the growth of a true woodland flora. Planting shrubs along the edges will help reduce light levels and may allow some woodland plants to grow.

- Understorey shrubs. If these are very dense, they will make the ground too shady for the growth of a diverse ground flora.

INTRODUCING WOODLAND FLORA

Where new woodlands are isolated from natural sources, woodland flora can be introduced by sowing direct, by planting bulbs or tubers, or by planting pot-grown plants. However plants are introduced, it's important that all seeds, bulbs, tubers or plants are of native provenance, which means that they originate from native British sources. Seeds or plants of British native provenance bought from nurseries and seed suppliers can be directly traced back to seed collected in the wild. These original seeds are used to produce stock plants in the nursery, from which seed and plants for retail sale are produced. Plants of local provenance, grown from seed originally collected from local wild plants, are even better, as many species have genetically distinct varieties which exist only small distances apart. Only buy plants from reputable nurseries who can guarantee that their plants, bulbs or tubers have been legitimately grown, and have not been dug up from the wild.

Alternatively, as with tree seeds, you can collect your own seed, provided you have permission to do so from the landowner. The seed can then either be sown direct onto the site, or sown to produce plants for planting out. Note that under the Wildlife and Countryside Act there over 60 species of native wild flowers from which it is illegal to gather seed, due to the rarity of the species. These include some woodland plants, including some orchids. It would be unusual to find these plants, but if in doubt, don't collect.

Woodland plants should never be dug up from existing sites, even with permission from the landowner. Under amendments to the Wildlife and Countryside Act, the digging up of some species, including bluebells, will become illegal. The Bluebell Recovery Project, sponsored by Landlife and the Mersey Forest Project, is working to protect existing bluebell woodlands from bulb thefts by creating a sustainable supply of native bluebell bulbs for legitimate sale in the future.

Woodland ground flora can be divided into three groups (Peterken, 1981). Some examples from each group are given below.

Group 1:

These are species normally associated with ancient woodland sites. Under natural conditions most of these produce little seed, and are slow to spread and colonise, which is why they are mainly limited to ancient woodland sites. Of the three groups, these are most exacting about site requirements, needing a closed canopy, the presence of leaf litter and absence of competition. Most of these species are available commercially as either seed, bulbs or plants. Ensure that bluebells are the species listed, and not the Spanish variety Hyacinthoides hispanica.

Bluebell	Hyacinthoides non-scripta syn. Endymion non-scriptus
Dog's mercury	Mercurialis perennis
Lesser celandine	Ranunculus ficaria
Moschatel	Adoxa moschatellina
Ramsons	Allium ursinum
Wood anemone	Anemone nemorosa
Wood sorrel	Oxalis acetosella

Group 2:

Fast-colonising species of recent woodlands and woodland edges. These are common at woodland edges, and persist at lower densities within the woodland in light shade. They tend to produce large quantities of seed, and are able to rapidly colonise bare ground. They are available commercially and are easy to grow from seed. Species include:

Ground ivy	Glechoma hederacea
Hedge woundwort	Stachys sylvatica
Herb robert	Geranium robertianum
Red campion	Silene dioica
Sweet woodruff	Galium odoratum
Wood avens	Geum urbanum

Group 3:

These include a large number of species which are common in woodland edges and hedgerows, but which are also common in other habitats. They produce large quantities of seed, and are easy to grow. Species include:

Betony	Stachys officinalis
Cow parsley	Anthriscus sylvestris
Foxglove	Digitalis purpurea
Hedge bedstraw	Galium mollugo
Hemp agrimony	Eupatorium cannabinum
Meadowsweet	Filipendula ulmaria

Introducing ground flora into new woodlands is not easy. Wild flowers are difficult to germinate and grow as they are very exacting in their requirements, unlike most garden flowers, which have been selected to tolerate a wide range of conditions and treatments.

You are unlikely to have success simply by scattering seed within the woodland, even if ground conditions look suitable. The seed of most woodland wild flowers needs vernalisation, or the action of winter frost, to make it germinate the following spring. During this time, much of the seed will be eaten by small mammals, with primrose and violet seed especially palatable to mice. Early spring sowing after cold treatment in a fridge may be possible, but the use of container-grown plants is usually better.

Use standard propagation techniques to germinate the seed in cells, trays or pots, and then grow them on until they are large enough to plant out. Species vary in their ease of germination, and experience in growing plants from seed is useful if you are going to try this method. The seed of most woodland plants should be sown in autumn, protected from mice and stored outside during the winter. Bring the trays into gentle warmth in February, and then prick out the plants into pots or cells as soon as the true leaves start to show. Grow them on during the summer, and plant out in the autumn.

Alternatively, some of the plants listed above, and other suitable species, are available as cell-grown plants or 'plugs'. These are plants grown in cells, which are despatched from the nursery as close-packed plants with rootballs of compost, which have been removed from the cells in which they were grown. Larger plants may be available in pots. The size of plant and method of despatch and packing will vary with the nursery, the season and the particular species.

wildflower plug

primrose

root plug

Depending on the level of care you can give in the field, it may be advisable to grow on wildflower 'plugs', until they are larger, sturdier plants which can compete more successfully. They can be grown on either in pots, or in a nursery bed, which in effect can become your stock bed from which you produce plants for the wild.

Planting out

Try to obtain the plants in spring and plant out as soon as conditions are suitable, preferably with the soil moist but beginning to warm up so that plants establish quickly. Choose suitable sites for the species, taking particular note of their requirements for shade.

Species from group 1 (above) should only be planted under closed canopy, where there is already bare ground. Choose sites which will not be trampled, perhaps under low spreading branches of trees or shrubs and away from paths and public access areas. Plant at about 9 plants per square metre, with the aim of encouraging the plants to form a clump from which they can spread into the surrounding woodland floor. For each plant, dig a larger hole than the size of the plug, incorporating some well-rotted leaf litter if the soil is lacking in organic matter. If possible, water the plants in well. Cover the surface of the plug with soil or leaf litter, otherwise the compost in the plug tends to dry out.

Plants from groups 2 and 3 should spread more quickly, and so can be planted at about 5 per square metre. Choose sites which are too shady to support the growth of grass, but which may support shade bearing plants such as ivy, nettle and bramble. Clear a patch a bit larger than the area you want to plant, and keep weeded until established.

Mark the locations of the planting areas on your woodland plan, and on the ground with pegs or stakes, so that you have a record of them, and can re-locate them to check on their progress and weed as necessary. Keep a look out for desirable wild plants which may appear, and don't necessarily weed out everything. As plants establish, you can divide clumps and replant in other parts of the woodland.

Muntjac deer can cause a lot of damage to ground flora, and as with young trees, may target nursery plants (p95). Rabbits can also be troublesome. Clumps of plants can be protected with loose piles of cut, dry brambles or with a 'cage' of chicken wire or similar. Old treeshelters cut into shorter lengths may also be effective. If browsing pressure from deer is very severe, it may be advisable to delay planting plans until effective deer control measures have been taken.

Bulbs

The woodland flora includes many plants which grow from bulbs. These are adapted to woodland conditions, as the bulbs produce an early burst of growth, flowering and reproduction before the canopy closes over in late spring. Bulbs are best planted during the autumn, as soon as you obtain them from the supplier. Ensure that any bulbs you buy are produced in nurseries, and are not taken from the wild. Only plant into the woodland once the canopy has closed, and grass growth has been eliminated by lack of light. A guide to planting is given below:

Bluebells (*Hyacinthoides non-scripta*)
  2-3 bulbs in holes 10cm (4") deep, 60cm (2') apart

Lesser celandine (*Ranunculus ficaria*)
  2-3 bulbs in holes 5cm (2") deep, 15cm (6") apart

Snowdrops (*Galanthus nivalis*)
  6 bulbs in holes 5cm (2") deep, 30cm (1') apart

Wild daffodils (*Narcissus pseudonarcissus*)
2-3 bulbs in holes 5cm (2") deep, 30cm (1') apart

Ramsons (*Allium ursinum*)
3-4 bulbs in holes 5cm (2") deep, 30 cm (1') apart

Wood anemone (*Anemone nemorosa*)
2-3 rhizomes, horizontally, 5cm (2") deep,
30cm (1') apart

Pests and diseases

Trees support a wide variety of other organisms, ranging from bacteria and viruses to birds and insects. Although these may affect individual trees in terms of health and lifespan, they rarely pose a threat to entire woodlands, due to the natural system of checks and balances present in a woodland ecosystem. Individual trees within a woodland which die from fungal attack or other causes provide habitats which are essential for the survival of many other organisms.

Treatment of pests and diseases is very important in commercial woodlands, orchards and for some amenity trees. Detailed information on pests and diseases are available in publications from the Forestry Commission (p114), and immediate advice is available over the phone from the Tree Advice Trust (p115), who also issue an occasional series of 'Tree Damage Alerts', which contain topical advice on many aspects of tree care.

The Asian Longhorn Beetle (see below) is currently causing concern.

PESTS

Mammals

Voles, rabbits, hares, deer and domestic stock can all severely damage young trees, including newly planted trees, naturally regenerated trees, and coppice shoots. Methods of protection are given on pages 82-92.

The main threat to established trees is from the grey squirrel, which can severely damage or kill trees between 5 and 40 years old, by stripping the bark anywhere on the main stem from the base to the crown. Woodlands dominated by beech, oak, sycamore and sweet chestnut are most vulnerable. Woodlands containing these species, but which are dominated by less vulnerable species are less likely to be attacked. Damage occurs between the end of April and the end of July, with the worst damage occurring about the third week in June. Damage is thought to be caused by frustrated young males with insufficient territory.

Where populations of squirrels reach 12 or more per hectare, control measures need to be taken. The aim should be to reduce the population to about 2 dominant males per hectare, who will keep out invaders. If the entire population is destroyed, other squirrels will quickly move in. Squirrels have no natural predators, and the only effective method of control is to use hoppers baited with grain treated with Warfarin. Control should start from March 15th, well before damage commences. There are strict regulations regarding the use of Warfarin and a National Proficiency Test Certificate is required for its use. Advice should be sought from the local office of the Forestry Commission, who will also have details of any local Grey Squirrel Management Group.

Deer populations have increased rapidly in the last few decades, and they are over-abundant in many areas. Deer can cause damage to young trees through browsing of foliage and fraying of the bark. Muntjac deer can also cause significant damage to woodland flora. Although newly planted trees can be protected (p87), the only way to ensure the success of natural regeneration, coppicing and the development of woodland flora is by culling of the deer population. This will only be effective if neighbouring areas are similarly managed, as deer can range over large areas. Contact your local office of the Forestry Commission for advice.

Insects

Most outbreaks of insect pests collapse as parasites and predators reach effective population levels. Insects and insect borne diseases are rarely a problem in mixed woodlands, although particular species may be vulnerable. Dutch Elm Disease, which caused the loss of most elms in England in the mid-1970s, was caused by a pathogen carried by the elm bark beetle.

The Asian Longhorn Beetle is currently causing concern as it can attack and kill healthy trees. The larvae feed under the bark and then burrow into the wood, and most hardwood species are at risk. Symptoms include foliage turning yellow and/or red, and premature leaf drop. Also look for piles of coarse sawdust at the base of the tree or where branches meet the trunk. Plant Health Regulations were brought into force in 1999 to try and stop further import of this beetle via wood packaging from China and elsewhere. Contact your local tree officer, Forestry Commission office or the Tree Advice Trust (p115) for advice.

The best way to keep insect populations in balance is to encourage insect-eating birds through provision of habitat within the woodland. Nesting boxes are a useful way to encourage bird species, especially when the woodland is young and lacks natural nest sites.

Pruning

This section outlines basic pruning of young trees during the establishment phase. Pruning and surgery of large and mature trees should only be carried out by fully trained workers.

FORMATIVE PRUNING

Young trees can be pruned to encourage strong upright growth and reduce side branching. This is important for trees grown for timber, but is not necessary on other trees. The amount of side branching will vary with the species, and with the distance apart which trees are planted. Closely planted trees produce fewer side branches. Trees grown singly in open ground tend to produce a much more branching, rounded shape.

The desire to produce natural looking wooded areas with a variety of tree shape and form needs to be balanced against the requirement to get trees established quickly. Pruning of side branches of most major woodland species including ash, oak, beech, lime, poplar and cherry produces strong upward growth. This has the advantage of quickly getting the leader up out of reach of vandals and deer. It also reduces the length of time when the developing woodland is at the 'thicket' stage, which many people find unattractive. In parks and other public access areas thickets are often viewed as 'overgrown areas' which tend to have negative associations of attracting unsocial behaviour. On the other hand, low branches and thickets may have practical uses in reducing access and vandalism, and may be desirable for screening, shelter from the wind, and noise reduction.

On balance, the need to establish trees quickly is usually the most important factor in successful woodland establishment, and selective pruning will help. Shrubs and thickets of growth can be encouraged at the edges of the planted area and in places away from public access, where their wildlife value will anyway be higher. Concentrate on getting clear-stemmed trees growing in the most visible areas, within view of paths, roads and other access areas. On sites where the value of tree planting is questioned, a band or clump of clear-stemmed trees will often be seen as enhancing the landscape, whereas an 'overgrown' thicket will not.

Pruning as an activity is also useful because it involves looking closely at the trees and encourages other aspects of aftercare. For many voluntary groups the labour intensive nature of pruning is a not a problem.

The best time for pruning oak, ash and cherry is between mid June to mid August, as this reduces the chance of bacterial or fungal infection. In the dormant seasons wounds are slow to heal and susceptible to damage by frost. Other species can be pruned at the same time, or between September and December. Never prune during the early growing season of February to May, when the sap is rising fast. Don't prune every tree, but choose the strongest growing, most upright ones of each species, leaving others to branch more freely and create structural diversity. Leading shoots which have forked due to damage or browsing should be pruned to leave a single leader. Trees which have been heavily browsed by deer and have formed a bushy top should be cut back to the main stem to encourage a single leader to emerge.

Side branches should be removed before they reach 2.5cm (1") in diameter, using a cut as shown below. To promote very fast growth, for example with ash or cherry, start two to three years after planting and prune away the side branches quite severely, leaving a clear stem about half the height of the tree. The developing crown can be balanced by tip-pruning the strongest branches, except the leader, to inhibit their growth, and severely pruning the weaker branches to stimulate vigorous growth.

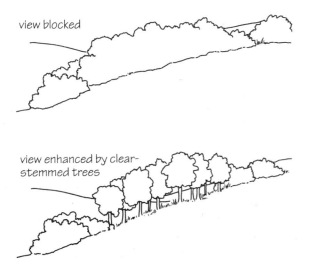

view blocked

view enhanced by clear-stemmed trees

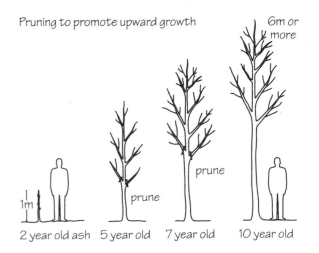

Pruning to promote upward growth

1m

2 year old ash   5 year old   7 year old   10 year old

prune

prune

6m or more

Pruning of side branches from the stem can be repeated every other year until the tree is about 10 years old, aiming for a crown of branches about one third the height of the tree. Long-handled pruning saws or treetop pruners (p36) will be necessary to reach the side branches. New shoots in the trunk, called epicormics, can be rubbed off or cut away with a sharp knife. In this way it's quite possible for an ash or cherry to grow to at least 6m (20') height within 10 years. Pruning should stop when the trunk has a diameter at breast height (dbh) of about 12cm (5"). By selecting and pruning trees in this way you can quickly add diversity to the woodland, and encourage the growth of particular individuals or stands of trees which become 'feature trees' within the wood. To encourage the dominance of selected trees, removal of nearby trees may be advisable.

Prune side branches as shown. Don't cut too close, or you will damage the main stem. On most branches, and particularly those the tree is preparing to shed, the 'branch collar' is visible (see below). Always make the pruning cut to the outside of the branch collar position. On the other hand, don't leave a 'coat peg', where rot can start. Aim to cut the branches at a stage when they can still be cut through with secateurs or pruners, either long-handled or treetop type for high reach. Pruning saws, both pocket size and long handled can also be used. If the branches are too big to be cut this way, you have left it too late.

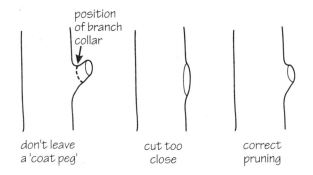

position of branch collar

don't leave a 'coat peg'   cut too close   correct pruning

CUTTING LARGER BRANCHES

You may need to cut larger branches which are overhanging paths or tracks, or to remove branches which are unsafe. Branches over about 15cm (6") diameter should only be cut by trained and experienced people.

Never cut inside the position of the branch collar. On decaying and dead branches this can be clearly seen, where it forms a natural barrier to protect the live tissue as the branch decays. Whether you are pruning live, dying or dead branches, always leave the branch collar intact.

branch collar →

Cut branches over about 25mm (1") in three stages, as shown. If you try to saw through them with one cut, they are likely to break and pull off a strip of bark, which damages the trees.

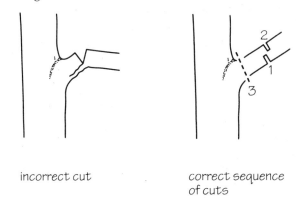

incorrect cut   correct sequence of cuts

Make the first cut about one third of the way through the branch from the bottom, but not so far that the saw binds. Make the second cut as shown, to sever the branch, leaving a projecting stub. Finally trim the stub with a third cut, starting at the top.

Don't leave a snag or stub. At best, this will only produce a mass of unsightly regrowth. More often, stubs die back, providing a foothold for infection and rot which can then be more easily transmitted to the rest of the tree.

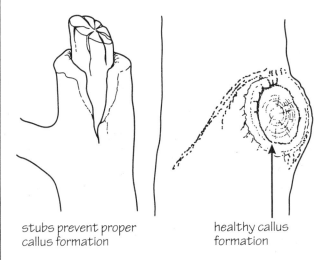

stubs prevent proper callus formation   healthy callus formation

Wound treatment

There is normally no need to treat cuts and wounds in trees with a wound paint, which in the past was recommended for the sealing of wounds against fungal attack. If the tree is healthy and the pruning cuts have been made cleanly and correctly, no further treatment should be necessary. The branch collar forms a protection boundary to prevent the inward spread of pathogens.

Treatment after pruning may be necessary on fruit trees, for example plums, which are prone to infection with silver leaf disease if pruning cuts are left untreated.

Thinning and selection

There is a direct relationship between the size of the crown and the stem diameter of the tree. Without sufficient crown to generate food, the stem will remain thin, and growth of the tree will stagnate, resulting in stands of crowded, spindly trees.

If planting has been closely spaced, as advised for quick establishment, the young woodland must be thinned to allow sufficient space for trees to continue to thrive. The old forestry rule is that the stem thickness (dbh) in inches should equal the radius of the crown in feet. For example, a tree with a dbh of 8 inches should have a crown of radius 8 feet, or diameter 16 feet.

Thinning should start about 10 years after planting for trees planted at 2m spacings, with successive thinning operations about every 10 years following. Trees planted at 3m spacings may not need thinning until about 20 years after planting. Table 7b (below) gives the recommended spacings for commercial production of various timber species. Although not directly applicable to mixed amenity woodlands, the table gives a guide to the amount of thinning which may be appropriate.

FELLING CONSIDERATIONS

The first thinning may require felling trees up to about 10cm (4") stem diameter, although size will vary greatly according to the site, spacing, species mix and other factors. Some trees may have put on little height or stem growth, having been out-competed by other trees. Other trees, particularly fast-growing species such as willow, may have grown to over 10cm (4") stem diameter, and depending on the purpose of the planting, may need thinning out to make space for slower growing, longer lived species.

In commercial crops, thinning requirements will be dictated by commercial considerations.

In addition to the safety points below, refer to those in chapter 4.

1 Think through carefully all the aspects of the work. This includes not only felling, but also removal of the cut material as necessary.

2 Study the tree to decide on likely directions of fall. The weight of the crown is a major factor in determining the direction of fall. Make sure that escape routes are cleared of bramble and other obstructions.

Table 7b: A guide to stocking and thinning rates for broadleaved trees

SPECIES	STOCKING	1st THINNING	LAST THINNING	ROTATION
Oak	3100	200 (7.1m)	90 (10.5m)	120-160
Beech	3100	250 (6.3m)	120 (9.1m)	95-140
Ash	2500	350 (5.3m)	150 (8.2m)	65-75
Sweet chestnut	2500	250 (6.3m)	190 (7.3m)	60-70
Sycamore	2500	350 (5.3m)	170 (7.7m)	60-70
Cherry	1100	250 (6.3m)	160 (7.9m)	50-70

Notes:

STOCKING This is the initial stocking rate given as number of trees per hectare.

1st THINNING This is the number of trees selected to grow on at the first thinning, given as number of trees per hectare, with average spacing between trees in metres.

LAST THINNING This is the number of final crop trees after the last thinning, given as number of trees per hectare, with average spacing between trees in metres.

ROTATION This is age for felling, to optimise timber production. In woodlands for wildlife and amenity, most trees which reach maturity can be retained and may live for up to 3 times the timber rotation. Very old trees and dead standing or fallen timber have high ecological value.

The edges of woodlands should be thinned less intensively than the sheltered inner part of the wood. Recently thinned trees are liable to windblow for a season or more, and the denser woodland edge is important as a windbreak.

3 Ensure there are no obstacles, such as stumps or boulders, over which the cut tree may fall, causing the butt end to spring upwards.

4 Check for overhead cables.

5 Be aware of present or imminent weather conditions. Don't work in heavy rain or strong wind. Take great care on slopes.

6 Put up warning signs or rope off areas and post look-outs in order to keep unauthorised people out of the area.

7 Don't work alone, but ensure that no-one else enters the danger zone while cutting is in progress.

8 Keep a safe distance of at least three tree lengths from other thinning operations.

9 Unless otherwise directed, leave as low a stump as possible. This is particularly important with slender saplings and coppice shoots. If these are felled with one oblique stroke, the sharply pointed stub that results presents a dangerous hazard.

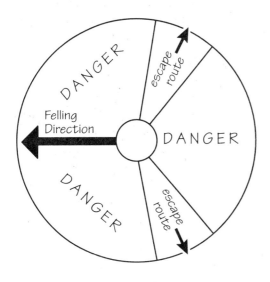

Thinning and other felling should be done in late autumn and winter, from October to February. At this time the trees are less sappy and are easier to cut and handle than in the growing season.

On wet sites you may have to work in late summer or autumn to minimise soil damage. Avoid work during spring and early summer, which is the main nesting and flowering season.

Normally you can leave the cut stumps untreated, and allow them to produce weak coppice growth. If a clear woodland floor is required for access or to encourage ground flora, treat the cut stumps with herbicide (p102), or dig them out.

FELLING SMALL TREES

Wear suitable clothing (p34) and a protective helmet.

Trees with a stem diameter of about 7.5cm (3") at the base can be felled by cutting straight through, using either a billhook or a bowsaw. Note that the 'front' of the tree is the side on which it is intended to fall, and the 'back' is the opposite side.

Bowsaw

The bowsaw is the safest and most versatile felling tool, and is best for most work on small trees.

Crouch or kneel to one side of the tree, in order to saw through from the back.

Make the cut level or angled slightly downward in the direction of fall. Using the full length of the blade, saw with easy relaxed strokes.

If the tree starts to twist, or as it settles back, use your other hand to push it in the direction of fall. Saw faster as the tree falls to minimise the risk of the stem splitting. Keep sawing to sever the stem.

Billhook

As a felling tool, the billhook is best used on light coppice material and multi-stemmed shrubs where a bowsaw is awkward. Don't wear a glove on the hand holding the tool, but a thick protective glove on the other hand is advisable.

Position yourself to the side of the tree, far enough back to achieve a full swing without endangering yourself. Standing allows a more powerful stroke, but crouching or kneeling may be necessary to avoid obstructions. Unless the tree is leaning heavily, you will be cutting into the front of the tree. Use the billhook one-handed, controlling the descent of the tree with the other hand, placed well up the stem for safety.

Don't try to cut directly across the grain. For small stems which can be severed with one blow, make a slightly upward-sweeping stroke. Avoid cutting downward, or you will drive the hook into the ground and dull or chip the edge. If the cut results in a sharply pointed stub, trim it immediately.

Cut thicker stems by notching, as shown. Progressively enlarge the notch with downward and upward strokes until you can finish off with an upward stroke. Keep out of the way of the tree as it falls.

FELLING LARGER TREES

Trees over 150mm (6") in diameter should only be felled by experienced workers. See *Woodlands* (BTCV 1988) for details.

Coppicing

Coppicing can commence from about seven years after planting, depending on the species, rate of growth and other factors. Coppicing is an ancient way of managing trees, which keeps them small and easy to harvest with hand tools, producing poles, firewood and other material. Coppice woods which are managed in rotation are rich in wildlife.

Once started, coppicing requires a commitment to long-term management, in order to keep to the coppice rotation. Hazel is normally cut every 7-10 years, sweet chestnut every 15 years, and oak and ash every 23-25 years. This will vary according to growth, the required size of the material for marketing purposes, and other factors. See the table on page 15 for further details.

Coppice woods are very suitable for volunteer involvement, as they can be managed with hand tools and produce materials which can be used within the wood for fencing or footpath work, as well as sold locally for garden poles, pea sticks and so on.

Coppice is normally cut between October and February.

INITIAL COPPICING

Coppice will not regrow if shaded by other trees, so if within a woodland, a reasonable sized area needs to be cut. These areas are called coupes, and should be planned at planting time, so they form a simple pattern which fits the rotation and is easy to implement. The minimum size of coupe should be an area of about 1000 square metres, preferably in a square shape to maximise sunlight and

benefits to habitat. Avoid long, thin or convoluted shapes. Smaller areas can be cut at edges of woodlands or along rides or glades, but they will not develop the ground flora and other wildlife which larger coupes can support.

Small patches of trees, mixed species or even individuals can be coppiced where the aim is to produce a small crop of pea sticks or bean poles. Hedges can be managed by coppicing sections in rotation, and using temporary fencing as necessary. Small areas of woodland, often known as 'copses' (coppices), can be divided into two coupes and managed entirely as coppice.

Coppicing can begin at the end of the establishment phase, which is when trees are growing vigorously and have no need of weeding or other regular maintenance. This should be about five years after planting. Hazel naturally produces many shoots, and should have produced a reasonable clump of stems at this stage. Other species will only have produced multiple stems if they were intentionally cut back at planting to grow this way, or if they were damaged and then cut back. Any single stemmed tree, such as ash, lime, sycamore or willow can be cut back at this stage with loppers or a small bowsaw, to stimulate multiple stems. Cut as close to the ground as possible, to encourage shoots to grow from the root collar area of the stem. If you cut higher, the stool can become unstable as it develops.

regrowth after first coppicing

Slower growing species such as oak, beech and hornbeam may need to be left a few more years before coppicing is started.

Regrowth is vulnerable to deer damage. One method of protecting the young shoots is to make a wigwam shaped structure of cut branches around the new stool, with blackthorn the most effective material. Bramble can be woven amongst sparser or non-spiny branches to make a barrier. Successful coppicing is difficult where deer numbers are high, and particularly in small coppice coupes where there is little other available fodder.

For details on managing established coppice, refer to *Woodlands* (BTCV, 1988).

Conservation and the volunteer worker

BTCV is the largest practical conservation organisation in the UK. It supports more than 85,000 volunteers from all sections of the community in activities to protect and improve the environment. With more than 110 offices around the UK, BTCV is able to work in a range of areas carrying out different activities. The Practical Handbooks series is one of the ways of helping to ensure that work undertaken by BTCV, volunteers and other conservationists is to the highest standard.

To ensure the success of any conservation project, it is important to establish:

*   Whether it is a worthwhile conservation project. Any work to be carried out should respond to a real need which is directly related to a broad framework of development. In terms of conservation, this means that projects should be undertaken as integral parts of site management plans, not as isolated exercises. The prime purpose of the work should also be made clear. For instance is it to improve local wildlife habitats or to improve access to the countryside?

*   That the work is suitable for volunteers. Volunteers cannot successfully tackle all types of work and they should not be involved where there is a risk of serious accident or injury, where machines can do the same job more effectively and for a lower cost, or where the skills required are beyond their capabilities. The latter can be overcome if professional training is provided so that a situation can be avoided where volunteers become dispirited or the work is not done to a high standard.

*   Where the project will take place and how much time it will take to complete. Once this has been done it is necessary to establish whether there are any hazards and risks associated with the site.

*   Whether the work should be done by paid staff. Voluntary service should not replace paid, local labour but complement it. Employers should make sure in advance that the position of volunteers and paid workers is clear with respect to any relevant labour unions.

Volunteers should not be regarded as providing 'free labour'. Someone has to pay for transport, materials, tools, insurance, refreshments and any accommodation charges. Before each party makes a commitment to a project it should be clear who is to pay for what. While volunteers may willingly fund their own work, clients should be prepared to contribute and should not assume that all volunteers, who are already giving their time and effort, will be able to meet other expenses out of their own pockets. Several grant-aiding bodies may help pay the cost of environmental and conservation projects. For details of grants and awards, contact BTCV at the address below. Comprehensive information is available in publications by the Charities Aid Foundation (see page 114).

It is important that volunteer workers are covered by public liability insurance for any damage or injury they may cause to third party property or to the public. Cover of at least two million pounds is recommended. Additional insurance to compensate the volunteer for injury to him or herself or to other volunteers on a project should also be considered. Specially tailored insurance is available through BTCV's own Group Membership Scheme. Contact the Local Groups Unit at the address below.

The volunteer group organiser should visit the work site well before the project to check that it is suitable and that volunteers will not be exploited, and to plan the best size of working party and the proper tools and equipment. Volunteers should be advised in advance on suitable clothing for the expected conditions, they should be physically fit and come prepared for work. Above all, individuals should genuinely want to volunteer – those 'press-ganged' into volunteering may do more harm than good and will not enjoy the benefits associated with volunteering. Young volunteers need more supervision and are best suited to less strenuous jobs, and it is recommended that where they are involved, the project should emphasise education. Recent legislation, including The Children Act, gives comprehensive guidance on supervisory ratios and other means to safeguard the welfare of young people. The recommendations of the Home Office report *Safe from harm*, should also be followed, and for any activities in remote areas, organisers should also be fully aware of the Adventure Activities Licensing Regulations.

Volunteer group organisers and clients should keep records of the work undertaken: the date of the project, jobs done, techniques used, number of volunteers and details of any notable events including accidents, unusual 'finds', publicity etc. Such information makes it easier to handle problems or queries which may arise after the project. It also provides a background on the project site for future visits, supplies practical data by which the site management plan can be evaluated and allows an assessment to be made of the volunteer effort.

As well as directly managing project work, whether for a day or more, BTCV supports volunteers indirectly through the local group service, runs a year round programme of training courses and organises hundreds of conservation working holidays in the UK and abroad. To find out more about what opportunities are available please write to: BTCV, 36, St Mary's Street, Wallingford, Oxon OX10 0EU.

Conservation and amenity organisations

This is a list of some of the organisations in the UK which are involved with trees, woodlands and other environmental matters. The BTCV web site (www.btcv.org) provides links to a large number of environmental organisations throughout the world.

Arboricultural Association
Ampfield House , Ampfield,
Hampshire SO51 9PA
Tel:01794 368717
www.trees.org.uk

Brogdale Horticultural Trust
Brogdale Road, Faversham, Kent ME13 8XZ
www.brogdale.org.uk

Charities Aid Foundation
Kings Hill, West Malling, Kent ME19 4TA
Tel: 01732 520000

Common Ground
PO Box 25309 , London NW5 1ZA
www.commonground.org.uk

The Community Forests
www.communityforest.org.uk

The Composting Association
Ryton Organic Gardens,
Ryton-on-Dunsmore,
Coventry CV8 3LG
Tel: 024 7630 8222
www.compost-uk.org.uk

Council for the Protection of Rural England (CPRE)
Warwick House,
25 Buckingham Palace Road,
London SW1W 0PP
Tel: 020 7976 6433
www.greenchannel.com/cpre

Countryside Agency (England)
John Dower House, Crescent Place, Cheltenham,
Glos GL50 3RA
Tel: 01242 521381
www.countryside.gov.uk

Countryside Council for Wales
Plas Penrhos, Fford Penrhos, Bangor,
Gwynedd LL57 2LQ
Tel: 01248 385500
www.ccw.gov.uk

English Nature
Northminster House, Peterborough PE1 1UA
Tel: 01733 455000
www.english-nature.org.uk

Environment Council
212 High Holborn, London WC1V 7VW
Tel: 0207 242 1180
www.the-environment-council.org.uk

Farming and Wildlife Advisory Group
National Agricultural Centre,
Stanley, Kenilworth,
Warwickshire CV8 2RX
Tel: 024 7669 6699
www.fwag.org.uk

Forestry and Arboricultural Safety and Training Council (FASTCo)
231 Corstorphine Road,
Edinburgh EH12 7AT
Tel: 0131 334 8083
www.fastco.gb.com

Forestry Commission
231 Corstorphine Road, Edinburgh EH12 7AT
Tel: 0131 334 0303
www.forestry.gov.uk

Forestry Contracting Association Ltd
Dalfling, Blairduff, Inverurie,
Aberdeenshire AB51 5LA
Tel: 01467 651368
www.fcauk.com

Game Conservancy
Burgate Manor, Fordingbridge,
Hampshire SP6 1EF
Tel: 01425 652381
www.game-conservancy.org.uk

The Greenwood Trust
Station Road, Coalbrookdale, Telford,
Shropshire TF8 7DR
Tel: 01952 432769
www.greenwoodtrust.demon.co.uk

Landlife
National Wildflower Centre,
Court Hey Park, Liverpool L16 3NA
Tel: 0151 737 1819
www.landlife.org.uk

Lantra (national training organisation for the
land based sector)
Lantra Connect, National Agricultural Centre,
Kenilworth, Warwickshire CV8 2LG
Tel: 0345 078007
www.lantra.co.uk

National Small Woods Association (NSWA)
3 Perkins Beach Dingle, Stiperstones,
Shropshire SY5 0PF
Tel: 01743 792644
www.woodnet.org.uk/nswa

National Urban Forestry Unit
The Science Park, Stafford Road,
Wolverhampton WV10 9RT
Tel: 01902 828600
www.nufu.org.uk

Ordnance Survey
Romsey Road, Maybush, Southampton SO16 4GU
Tel: 023 8079 2000
www.ordsvy.gov.uk

Ramblers Association
1-5 Wandsworth Road
London SW8 2XX
Tel: 020 7339 8500
www.ramblers.org.uk

Royal Society for the Protection of Birds (RSPB)
The Lodge, Sandy, Beds SG19 2DL
Tel: 01767 680551
www.rspb.org.uk

Scottish Natural Heritage
12 Hope Terrace, Edinburgh EH9 2AS
Tel: 0131 447 4784
www.snh.org.uk

Shell Better Britain Campaign
King Edward House, 135a New Street,
Birmingham B2 4QJ
Tel: 0121 248 5900
www.sbbc.co.uk

Sustrans Ltd
35 King Street, Bristol BS1 4DZ
Tel: 0117 926 8893
www.sustrans.org.uk

Thrive *(formerly Horticultural Therapy)*
The Geoffrey Udall Centre, Beech Hill,
Reading RG7 2AT
Tel: 01189 885688
www.thrive.org.uk

The Tree Advice Trust
Arboricultural Advisory and
Information Service, Alice Holt Lodge,
Wrecclesham,
Farnham GU10 4LH
Tree Helpline: 0897 161147
www.treeadviceservice.org.uk

Tree Council
51 Catherine Place, London SW1E 6DY
Tel: 020 7828 9928
www.treecouncil.org.uk

Woodland Trust
Autumn Park, Grantham,
Lincolnshire NG31 6LL
Tel: 01476 581111
www.woodland-trust.org.uk

Grants and training

Addresses for further information, where not listed here, are given on pages 114-115.

Grants

The main grant available in England, Scotland and Wales for woodland planting and management is the Woodland Grant Scheme, which is outlined below. Many other grants may be available for projects which include tree planting or management, but details are not included here as these vary across national boundaries, with designated areas and other factors. Grants may be available which are aimed at encouraging local community action for example, or for aims such as landscape enhancement, of which tree planting may be a part. Sites of high ecological value may also attract grant aid.

For voluntary groups and individuals, your best point of contact is the tree officer/conservation officer at your local authority, or your local BTCV office. BTCV publish an annual list titled *Information on grants and awards open to local groups, communities and schools*.

The Countryside Agency (England) publish *Grants and payment schemes – a guide to grants and payments from the Countryside Agency*. The Countryside Council for Wales or Scottish Natural Heritage should be contacted for information relating to their areas.

For information on grants for tree planting and woodland management in Northern Ireland, contact the Department of the Environment Northern Ireland and the Forest Service of the Department of Agriculture in Northern Ireland.

THE WOODLAND GRANT SCHEME

The Woodland Grant Scheme provides incentives for people to create and manage woodlands on sites all over Great Britain. It is administered by the Forestry Commission.

Grants for new woodlands

Normally the woodland would have to be 0.25 hectare in area and at least 15m wide to be eligible, but smaller woods may qualify if the aims of the scheme are met.

Woodland Grant Scheme (WGS) Rate of grant (2000)

	Conifers	Broadleaves
Woods less than 10ha	£700 per ha	£1350 per ha
Woods more than 10ha	£700 per ha	£1050 per ha

Grants for new planting are paid in two instalments – 70% when planting is finished, and 30% after five years.

Supplements are available for new planting in priority areas, which include the Better Land Supplement for planting on some agricultural land, and the Community Woodland Supplement, for woodland creation for informal recreation close to urban areas. The Locational Supplement is available in certain areas.

North of the Forth-Clyde valley in Scotland, native pinewoods of natural character normally qualify for the rate paid for broadleaved planting.

Short rotation coppice of poplar or willow may attract grants.

Requirements for grants:

To receive the full rate of planting grant and supplements, planting of at least 2250 trees per hectare is required. For broadleaves, a density of 1100 trees per hectare may be acceptable in the following circumstances:

- For small scale planting. This would normally apply to individual broadleaved woodlands of less than 3 hectares, where there is limited potential for timber production.

- For planting broadleaves, where they form the amenity component of mainly coniferous planting schemes.

- For new native woodlands on appropriate semi-natural habitats or in areas adjacent to existing semi-natural woodlands.

The species proposed must suit the site and meet management aims. Where nature conservation is an important aim, this will normally mean using the species which are, or might have been, native to the site.

Open ground within woodland is desirable for management and environmental reasons. The amount and location of open ground must be agreed with the Forestry Commission, who may pay grant on it up to a limit of 20% of the whole area getting grant. i.e. if the area enclosed by the boundary of the application is 10 hectares and grant is to be paid over the whole area, then 2 hectares can be left as open ground and 8 hectares must be planted.

Grant may be available to plant woody shrubs such as hazel, buckthorn or juniper, provided they are appropriate to the area, and comprise no more than 10% of the whole area getting grant.

Planting grant and supplements are payable for the planting of new coppice stools.

Farm Woodland Premium Scheme

Under the Farm Woodland Premium Scheme (FWPS), also administered by the Forestry Commission, annual payments are made by the Agriculture Departments to compensate for agricultural income foregone through tree planting. Farmers can apply for either the Woodland Grant Scheme (WGS) alone, or both the WGS and FWPS. It's not possible to apply for the FWPS alone because the environmental and silvicultural standards of the WGS must be satisfied before an FWPS scheme can be approved.

GRANTS FOR EXISTING WOODLAND

Grants for restocking by planting or natural regeneration

Grants are paid for the restocking of woodlands after felling or windblow, whether by planting or regeneration. Grants are also paid for the management and improvement of woodlands and for the exclusion of stock from certain woods.

Rates of restocking grants (2000)

| Conifers | £325 per ha | normally planted 2250/ha |
| Broadleaves | £525 per ha | normally planted 1100/ha |

Natural regeneration provides an alternative to planting when restocking areas in existing woodlands and for creating new woodlands by extending from an existing woodland. Where natural regeneration is both practical and appropriate, the Forestry Commission will not normally agree to proposals for planting. If natural regeneration is not appropriate, it will not be grant aided.

There are two elements to the grant for natural regeneration:

- A Discretionary Payment of 50% of the agreed costs of work necessary to encourage the natural regeneration

- A Fixed Payment equivalent to the rate for restocking.

The Discretionary Payment might cover the cost of fencing or ground preparation. The Fixed Payment can be claimed when an adequate stocking has been achieved, when the young trees are around 30-45cm tall, healthy and well-established. There needs to be at least 1100 trees per hectare but usually more will be required. For native woodlands, a clumped distribution may be preferable.

If no work is necessary to encourage natural regeneration, you cannot get a Discretionary Payment, but you may be able to claim the Fixed Payment.

The Annual Management Grant

The Annual Management Grant may be available to help towards the cost of maintaining and improving woodlands, if the proposed work may do one or more of the following:

- Safeguard or enhance the existing special environmental value of a wood

- Improve woodlands which are below current environmental standards

- Create, maintain or enhance public access to woodlands.

The Woodland Improvement Grant

The Woodland Improvement Grant is a single payment made to encourage a range of work in existing woodlands:

- Work which will help to encourage informal public recreation in existing woodlands.

- Work which will help to bring undermanaged woodlands back into management.

- Work to encourage woodland biodiversity.

Livestock Exclusion Annual Premium

This may be payable to farmers to compensate for the loss of revenue from excluding livestock from woodlands. To be eligible, woodlands must be in a Less Favoured Area or an Environmentally Sensitive Area.

Training

BTCV

BTCV provide a wide range of training courses and events on many aspects of environmental and countryside management throughout England, Northern Ireland, Scotland and Wales.

Training is an integral part of BTCV activities, and most projects include an element of training. Information on special training courses and other training events organised by BTCV are available from local BTCV offices and from the Wallingford office (address on page ii).

The Environmental Trainers Network (ETN) is a network of organisations that provide short courses in a wide range of environmental matters. Details are available from the

Environmental Trainers Network, c/o BTCV Enterprises, Red House, Hill Lane, Great Barr, Birmingham B43 6LX Tel: 0120 358 2155.

BTCV also provides training leading to the attainment of Environmental National Vocational Qualifications (NVQs).

Current details on BTCV and ETN courses, and on Environmental NVQs are available on the BTCV website (www.btcv.org).

OTHER TRAINING PROVIDERS

The Countryside Agency, in association with the Countryside Council for Wales, publish an annual directory of short training courses in England and Wales entitled *The Countryside Training Directory*.

Local land-based colleges and colleges of agriculture provide short and long courses in many aspects of countryside management. Contact your local college for further information.

The National Small Woods Association (address on page 115) run workshops and other events concerned with the management of small woods, and can provide contacts for training in green woodwork and other woodland craft skills.

The Forestry Commission, through Forest Training Services, run an extensive range of training events designed for workers in the forest industry. Details are available from:

Forest Training Services
Head Office, Ae Village,
Parkgate, Dumfries DG1 1QB
Tel: 01387 860637
e-mail: forestry.training.services@forestry.gov.uk.

The Forestry and Arboricultural Safety and Training Council (FASTCo) are responsible for determining competence standards in all sectors and at all levels of forestry. FASTCo has a register of approved instructors, and publishes a range of safety guides covering all aspects of the industry.

For a full list of academic, professional and vocational courses related to the environment, consult the current Directory of Environmental Courses, published by the Environment Council, and available from the Council (p114), or from libraries.

Suppliers

This is a brief list of suppliers of tree planting products. Other firms may produce similar suitable products. Horticulture Week and Forestry and British Timber (monthly) are useful sources of information. Websites worth checking for products, services and links include:

www.the-hta.co.uk
   (the Horticultural Trades Association)
www.trees.org.uk
   (the Arboricultural Association)
www.woodnet.org.uk
   (network of UK producers and users of wood)
www.alphasearch.co.uk
   (forestry products and services)

Alba Trees plc
   Lower Winton, Gladsmiur, East Lothian EH33 2AI
   www.alba-trees.co.uk
   Tool for planting Rootrainer

Acorn Planting Products Ltd
   Little Money Road, Loddon, Norwich NR14 6JD
   Tel: 01508 528763
   e-mail: www.acorn-p-p.co.uk
   Treeshelters, shelterguards, gro-cones, mulching mats

Agricultural Polymers International Ltd
   Waverley House, Waverley Road,
   Gloucester GL2 0SZ
   Tel: 01452 521733
   www.agripol.co.uk
   Broadleaf P4 water-storing granules and root dip

Arid Lands Initiative
   Machpelah Works, Burnley Road,
   Hebden Bridge, West Yorkshire HX7 8AU
   Tel 01422 843807
   e-mail: oasis@aridlands.freeserve.co.uk
   Tree growing kits

BTCV Enterprises Ltd
   Conservation Centre, Balby Rd, Doncaster DN4 0RH
   Tel: 01302 572200
   www.btcv.org.uk
   Native provenance trees, shrubs and wildflowers, tools, tree planting products, clothing and books

Greentech
   PO Box 1, Boroughbridge, Yorkshire YO51 9NY
   Tel: 01423 324342
   e-mail: green-tech@zoo.co.uk
   Tree planting products including peat-free composts

Harrod Horticultural
   Pinbush Road, Lowestoft, Suffolk NR33 7NL
   Tel: 01502 583515   www.harrod.uk.com
   Garden netting, ground pegs, net ties, fleece

Melcourt Industries Ltd
   Eight Bells House, Tetbury, Glos GL8 8JG
   Tel: 01666 502711   www.melcourt.co.uk
   Peat-free composts

Plant Health Care
   Berkhamsted House, 121 High Street, Berkhamsted,
   Herts HP4 2DJ
   Tel: 01442 864431 e-mail: phcuk@aol.com
   MycorTree Root Dip and other mycorrhizal products

Ronaash Limited
   Kersquarter, Kelso, Roxburghshire TD5 8HH
   Tel: 01573 225757   www.ronaash.co.uk
   Rootrainers

Stanton Hope Limited
   11 Seax Court, Southfields, Laindon, Essex SS15 6LY
   Tel: 01268 419141
   Comprehensive range of clothing, tools, tree protectors, chainsaws, safety signs, chemicals, dye, sprayers, measures

Symbio
   38 Bookham Industrial Park, Church Road,
   Great Bookham, Surrey KT23 3EU
   Tel: 01372 456101
   www.symbio.co.uk
   MycoForce mycorrhizal and microbial products

J. Toms Ltd
   Grigg Lane, Headcorn, Ashford, Kent TN27 9XT
   Tel: 01622 891111
   e-mail: tomsties@compuserve.com
   Tree ties, guards, netting, mulch, tools

Tubex Limited
   Aberaman Park, Aberdare CF44 6DA
   Tel: 01685 888000
   www.tubex.com
   Tree guards.

Woodland Improvement and Conservation Ltd
   Newent Lane, Huntley, Royal Forest of Dean,
   Gloucestershire GL19 3HG
   Tel: 01452 832100
   www.woodland-improvement.co.uk
   Native and introduced trees, tools, accessories, books

Introduced trees for orchards, gardens and parks

Tree planting for forestry and wildlife has had a much shorter history than tree planting for fruit, shelter and pleasure. The earliest civilisations are partly defined by their ability to grow crops and plant trees in gardens and orchards. From the Garden of Eden onwards, there has been an urge to collect and plant useful and beautiful species of tree.

The Romans introduced the sweet chestnut, the cultivated apple, the medlar and other species (p2) to Britain. The temperate climate of the British Isles allows a huge variety of trees and shrubs from all over the world to be grown, and introduced species have provided a great impetus to gardening and the growing of trees. Our gardens, parks and streetscapes are characterised by the introduced species which they contain.

Most of our native 'forest' trees, such as ash, beech, lime and oak are too big or cast too dense a shade to be grown as garden trees. The smaller native trees such as rowan, crab-apple, hawthorn, holly and yew have been widely planted in gardens, parks, roadsides and churchyards, and many different cultivars have been identified and propagated for their particular foliage, fruit, flowers or form of growth.

Trees which are planted for mainly ornamental reasons also have important environmental benefits. Although native trees support the highest number of invertebrates, many introduced trees are also valuable for invertebrates, and may be of equal value for birds and some other organisms. This is because trees in urban areas, whether they are native or introduced, tend to support a range of generally common, though valuable, organisms. It is only the very ancient veteran native trees in parks and wood pastures, or the community of trees in the specialist, humid environment of a woodland where native trees have their highest ecological value. Introduced or native trees are equally valuable for reducing greenhouse gases, counteracting the heat-island effect of towns, reducing noise, filtering pollutants and making people feel better. In urban areas, introduced trees are certainly better than no trees at all.

Trees in towns and cities have much to cope with, including low humidity, high reflection from paved surfaces, air pollution, disturbed ground and poor drainage. Urban areas have higher temperatures and much lower humidity than surrounding rural areas, with conditions in some cities approaching those of the Mediterranean. Our native woodland trees are adapted to humid air, shelter and shade, and may not thrive in urban conditions. Introduced species or hybrids often have better resistance to drought, dry air, pollution and wind damage than native species, and as such are better suited to growing in towns and cities.

Introduced species greatly lengthen the season of flowering and fruiting, so that for birds, invertebrates and other organisms there is a greater range of food available throughout the year. Urban beekeepers consistently produce higher yields than rural beekeepers, because of the range of nectar available from introduced plants in parks and gardens, and because of the higher air temperatures. Many species of birds also thrive in the woodland-edge type habitat of the leafy suburbs.

Choosing and planting introduced trees

There is a huge range of trees available from garden centres, nurseries and specialist suppliers. Choice should be made according to the soil type, situation, space available and the purpose of the planting. There are many books available in libraries and bookshops which can be consulted for further advice, including the following:

The Tree and Shrub Expert
    Dr D G Hessayon (pbi Publications)

Garden Trees
    The Royal Horticultural Society (Dorling Kindersley)

The Hillier Manual of Trees and Shrubs
    Hillier (pocket edition also available).

Introduced trees are normally not available as small, two year, bare-root transplants, but are grown in the nursery for another year or two until they are 1.2-1.8m (4-6ft) in height. Some species also benefit from early pruning, which is best done in the nursery, to form a balanced head of growth. They are sold as either bare-root, root-balled (wrapped) or container-grown plants, depending on the species and the supplier. Garden centres normally sell container-grown plants. With ornamental trees, many purchasers want to plant for immediate impact, and at any time of year, and are willing to pay the much higher prices which older, container-grown stock commands. As with any tree, the shock from transplanting and the generally poor root:shoot ratio of standard trees (p67) means that such trees may be slow to establish and put on new growth. Choosing the smaller, younger and cheaper sizes available for any species will, given correct care, lead to the best establishment. Even for container-grown stock, planting in autumn is the best time of year.

When planting, follow the advice given on page 79 for pit planting. Tree roots spread and are mainly active in the top 60 cm (2') of soil, so generally dig a hole which is wider than it is deep. A hole 1m (3ft) square is not too large, and should be backfilled with a mixture of soil and compost. This forms a graded zone between the compost in the container and the surrounding soil, and encourages new roots to venture out of the compost and into the new ground. A circle of at least 1m (3ft) diameter around the tree must be kept free of grass for at least 3 years after planting.

Orchards

In the past, most farms and gardens, large and small, included an orchard of fruit trees. Before the days of cold storage and rapid transport, fruit was mainly limited to the types you could grow in your own locality. In Britain, as in other countries, hundreds of local fruit varieties were cultivated and identified, with areas having their own particular apples, pears, plums and other types of tree fruit.

Most private gardens have at least one fruit tree, but with cheap imports of fruit, private and commercial orchards have declined rapidly in recent decades. Many have been grubbed out and converted to agricultural use or building development. The charity Common Ground is active in promoting the saving of old orchards and the planting of new ones for community use. Common Ground publishes a series of *Orchards Advice Notes*, a newsletter *Orchards News*, and provides a useful forum for all those interested in community orchards. The Brogdale Horticultural Trust

in Kent comprises the National Fruit Collection, including the largest collection of apple varieties in the world. It offers training events, a fruit identification service and supplies a wide variety of fruit trees.

Fruit trees are available from garden centres and specialist nurseries, and many books are available on their cultivation and care. Fruit trees are grown on rootstocks which affect the growth and fruiting potential of the tree, with dwarfing rootstocks recommended for smaller gardens. For large gardens and orchards, standard or half-standard trees on semi-dwarfing rootstocks may be suitable. *The Fruit Expert* by Dr D G Hessayon (pbi Publications) gives clear details on the growing of tree and soft fruit.

One-year-old maiden trees, available bare-root from specialist suppliers, are the cheapest way to buy, but will require careful pruning for at least three years to form a balanced framework of branches. Two-year-old, partly trained trees are usually the best choice. Trees over four years old should be avoided, as they will be slow to establish.

Planting should follow standard advice (above and page 79). Staking is normally necessary at planting, and may need to be permanent for small bush trees. Trained trees, such as espaliers, will need appropriate supports. For the best crops, the ground under the fruit tree should be kept clear of other growth, especially grass. For orchards, bare ground is normally only appropriate for commercial growing, and most community orchards will include grasses and wild flowers. Fruit trees are prone to a variety of pests and diseases, and attention needs to be paid to their cultivation and care.

Bibliography

Tree planting and aftercare and related subjects, are covered by a wide range of published material. The list below includes publications to which reference has been made in the text, as well as other useful sources. Websites (p114) of the Forestry Commission and other organisations include publications lists and ordering information.

Broad, Ken (1998)
Caring for Small Woods
Earthscan Publications Ltd

Dewar, Sue M and Shawyer, Colin R (1996)
Boxes, Baskets and Platforms –
Artificial Nest Sites for Owls and other Birds of Prey
The Hawk and Owl Trust

Finch-Savage, W E (1998)
Farm Woodland Tree Seed
Horticulture Research International, Wellesbourne, Warwick

Garfitt, J E (1995)
Natural Management of Woods – Continuous Cover Forestry
John Wiley and Sons

Gordon, A G, Gosling, P G and Wang, B S P (1991)
Tree and Shrub Seed Handbook
International Seed Testing Association

Huxley, Anthony (1978)
An Illustrated History of Gardening
Paddington Press Ltd

Luscombe, Grant and Scott, Richard (revised 1998)
Wildflowers Work
Landlife

Mitchell, Alan (1988)
Trees of Britain and Northern Europe
Collins

National Small Woods Association (1998)
Small woods information pack
NSWA (address on page 115)

Peterken, G F (1981)
Woodland Conservation and Management
Chapman and Hall

Rackham, Oliver (revised 1990)
Trees and Woodlands in the British Landscape
Phoenix Giant

Read, Helen (2000)
Veteran Trees – A guide to good management
English Nature

Salt, Bernard (undated)
Gardening under Plastic
Batsford Gardening Books

Woodland Improvement and Conservation Ltd
Manual
Woodland Improvement & Conservation Ltd (p115)

COUNTRYSIDE AGENCY PUBLICATIONS

Available from Countryside Agency Postal Sales
Tel: 0870 120 6466

Growing in Confidence – Understanding People's Perceptions of Urban Fringe Woodlands
Countryside Commission (1995)

Regeneration around cities – The role of England's Community Forests
Countryside Agency (1999)

FORESTRY COMMISSION PUBLICATIONS

These are listed by author, and are available from Telelink Limited Tel: 01329 331345

Aldhous, J R and Mason W L (1994)
Forest Nursery Practice
Forestry Commission Bulletin 111

Evans, J (1984)
Silviculture of Broadleaved Woodland
Forestry Commission 62

Forestry Commission (1985)
Wildlife Rangers Handbook
Forestry Commission

Forestry Commission (1991)
Community Woodland Design – Guidelines
Forestry Commission

Gordon, A G (1992)
Seed Manual for Forest Seed
Forestry Commission Bulletin 83

Harmer, Ralph (1999)
Using Natural Colonisation to Create or Expand New Woodlands
Forestry Commission Information Note

Herbert, R; Samuel, S and Patterson, G (1999)
Using Local Stock for Planting Native Trees and Shrubs
Forestry Commission

Hibberd, B G (edit) (1989)
Urban Forestry Practice
Forestry Commission Handbook 5

Hodge, Simon J (1995)
Creating and Managing Woodlands around Towns
Forestry Commission Handbook 11

Hodge, Simon and Pepper, Harry (1998)
The Prevention of Mammal Damage to Trees in Woodland
Forestry Commission Practice Note

Kerr, Gary and Williams, Hugh V (1999)
Woodland Creation – Experience from the National Forest
Forestry Commission Technical Paper 27

MacKenzie, Neil A (1999)
*The Native Woodland Resource of Scotland
– A Review 1993-1998*
Forestry Commission Technical Paper 30

Morgan, John (1999)
Forest Tree Seedlings – Best Practice in Supply, Treatment and Planting   Forestry Commission Bulletin 121

Pepper, H W (1992)
Forest Fencing   Forestry Commission Bulletin 102

Pepper, H; Neil, D and Hemmings, J (1996)
Application of the chemical repellent Aaprotect to prevent winter browsing
Forestry Commission Research Information Note 289

Pepper, Harry and Currie, Fred (1998)
Controlling Grey Squirrel Damage to Woodlands
Forestry Commission Practice Note

Rodwell, John and Patterson, Gordon (1994)
Creating New Native Woodlands
Forestry Commission Bulletin 112

Williamson, D R (1992)
Establishing Farm Woodlands
Forestry Commission Handbook 8

Willoughby, Ian and Dewar, Jim (1995)
The use of Herbicides in the Forest
Forestry Commission Field Book 8

Willoughby, Ian and Clay, David (1996)
Herbicides for Farm Woodlands & Short Rotation Coppice
Forestry Commission Field Book 14

JOURNALS

Relevant journals on tree propagation, planting and management include the following:
Arboricultural Journal (Arboricultural Association quarterly publication)
Enact (English Nature quarterly journal)
Forestry and British Timber (monthly)
Horticulture Week (weekly)
Tree News (twice-yearly magazine from the Tree Council)

BTCV PUBLICATIONS

The BTCV Practical Handbook series was started in the 1970s, with most of the original titles remaining in print throughout, and new titles being added over the years. There is a rolling programme of revision with most Handbooks now in their second edition. BTCV welcomes feedback at any time on aspect of the Handbooks, whether the comments are general or detailed, practical or academic, complimentary or critical. Please contact:

Handbooks Editor
BTCV, 36 St Mary's Street, Wallingford,
Oxfordshire OX10 0EU
Tel: 01491 821600 Fax: 01491 839646
e-mail: information@btcv.org.uk
www.btcv.org

The Handbook series comprises:

Fencing (1986)
Sand Dunes (2nd edition, 1986)
Woodlands (2nd edition, 1988)
Toolcare (2nd edition, 2000)
Tree Planting and Aftercare (2000)
Footpaths (2nd edition, 1996)
Waterways and Wetlands (2nd edition, 1997)
Hedging (2nd edition, 1998)
The Urban Handbook (1998)
Dry Stone Walling (2nd edition, 1999)

Other BTCV publications relevant to this handbook, include the following:

British Trust for Conservation Volunteers (1999)
Forests for our Future

Conservation Volunteers Northern Ireland (1996)
Our Trees – A guide to growing Northern Ireland's native trees from seed

To order any of the Handbooks, or for details of other BTCV publications and merchandise, please contact:

BTCV Enterprises Ltd
Conservation Centre, Balby Rd, Doncaster DN4 0RH
Tel: 01302 572200   Fax: 01302 310167

Orders can also be placed through the BTCV website at www.btcv.org

Individual members and affiliated groups of BTCV receive the Conserver magazine, and have access to advice on many aspects of conservation volunteering, including organising a local group, health and safety advice, grants and insurance.

For further details please contact the information office at Wallingford (address above).

Glossary

Afforestation
The process of converting unforested land to forestry plantations.

Agroforestry
The growing of trees on land also used for crops or livestock.

Ancient woodland
A site that has been wooded continuously since at least AD1600.

Arboretum
Place where trees or shrubs are grown for their scientific or educational interest.

Arboriculture
The cultivation of trees and shrubs for ornamental, landscape or other objectives other than for timber production.

Bare-root tree
Tree lifted for planting without soil or compost around its roots.

Bast
Thin layer of tissue between the bark and the cambium, which carries leaf-sap downwards to the roots.

Beating up
Replacing failed plants after tree planting.

Bole
The stem or trunk of a tree.

Bolling
The permanent trunk of a pollard.

Branch bark ridge
A layer of compacted xylem tissue and wrinkled bark that forms a ridge in the angle where a branch and trunk meet, and serves as a natural protection boundary that resists decay.

Branch collar
A collar of tissue that forms around the base of a branch in some species, usually as the tree ages. With the branch bark ridge, this is one of the tree's main protection boundaries against decay.

Brash
(n) Small branches trimmed from the sides and top of a main stem. (v) To cut away the side branches of conifers to c.2m (6') to improve access or for fire protection.

Broadleaved trees
Deciduous and evergreen dicotyledon trees.

Bryophytes
Mosses and liverworts.

Buttress
Reinforcing projection near the base of the tree.

Callusing
The growth of new tissue across a wound (eg from pruning), which derives from living cells at the edge, and can protect the tree from bacterial and fungal decay.

Cambium
A layer of cellular tissue beneath the bark, in which the growth of bark and wood takes place.

Canker
On a branch or stem, a dead area which has been caused by bacterial or fungal attack.

Canopy
The uppermost layer of woodland structure, usually from 8-30m (25-100') above the ground. Includes the standard, emergent and understorey trees.

Chitted seed
Seed in which the radicle, or that part of the embryo which develops into the primary root, has just emerged.

Clone
A strain propagated vegetatively from a single individual.

Community Forest
12 urban areas in England designated by the Countryside Agency, where woodland creation and management is being encouraged, to deliver economic, social and enviromental benefits to local communities.

Coppice
(n) A deciduous broadleaved wood which is cut to the ground at regular intervals to produce many shoots from each stool. Also known as a copse. (v) To cut the shoots from a stool, from which more will grow.

Coppice with standards
A two-storey wood in which standard trees are grown among the coppice or underwood.

Cord
(n) Stack of wood, normally 8 x 4 x 4ft (2.7 x 1.2 x 1.2m), cut from the branches of trees and typically used for firewood or charcoal production. (v) To cut wood in appropriate lengths and stack in a cord.

Cordwood
Branches suitable for cutting into lengths equal to the cord width.

Coupe
A coppice plot cut on a regular basis, or a clear-felled area in a plantation. Also known as a panel.

Covert
A small wood, usually in the midst of farmland, managed primarily for game.

Crown
The spreading branches and foliage of a tree.

Cultivar
A cultivated variety, or sub-division, of a species, consisting of plants which differ in some way from the norm for that species.

Cutting
A small section of young shoot or root used to propagate a new plant.

Danger zone
The area within two tree lengths, in any direction, of a tree being felled.

Drip line
The ground below the outermost branches of a tree's crown, where most of the feeding roots are concentrated.

Emergent tree
A tree, the crown of which overtops other standards in the woodland canopy.

Feathered tree
A nursery stock tree with lateral shoots to near ground level.

Field layer
That part of the woodland structure containing herbaceous plants and undershrubs.

Flush
The first spurt of growth after winter when the buds break.

Forest
Originally a term for an area of land, not necessarily wooded, which was controlled by the Crown for deer-hunting. Forest Law applied in these areas. Now generally used to describe a large area of woodland, particularly plantations of coniferous trees, such as those managed by the Forestry Commission. See also Community Forests.

Formative pruning
The pruning of a young plant to achieve a desired shape.

Ground layer
That part of the woodland structure, up to about 10cm (4in) above ground, which contains bryophytes and the seedlings of plants of the higher layers.

Habitat
The place where an organism lives.

Hardwood
The timber of broadleaved trees.

Heartwood
The inner wood of larger branches and trunks, which no longer carries sap.

Hectare
A metric unit of area, 100 x 100m. Comprises 100 ares, each 10 x 10m. There are 2.47 acres to the hectare.

Heeling-in
Temporarily storing transplants or planting stock in a trench backfilled with earth.

High forest
Woodland dominated by full-grown trees suitable for timber.

Honeydew
Sticky substance produced by aphids, which can cause nuisance when it drips onto anything below.

Kerf
The cut made by a saw.

Layer
(n) A side shoot which roots to form a new but connected plant where it touches the ground. (v) To bend over and peg down a shoot so that it will take root.

Leader
The main top shoot of a tree.

Lop and top
See brash

Mast year
A year in which trees produce exceptionally large quantities of seed and fruit.

Mulching
The application of a suitable material to the surface of the soil to conserve moisture, stabilise soil temperature and suppress weed growth.

Mycorrhiza
A symbiosis between soil fungi and the roots of plants

Natural colonisation
The natural spread of trees by seed or suckers into unpreviously wooded ground.

Natural regeneration
The natural replacement or spread of trees by seed or suckers in already wooded ground.

Node
A swelling on a shoot which marks the position of a resting bud.

Nurse species
Hardy, quick-growing trees planted and managed for the purpose of sheltering less vigorous, less robust or more valuable tree species when they are young.

Orthodox seed
Tree seed which can be partially dried and stored.

Park
Originally, land enclosed for the keeping of semi-wild animals. Later, a rural or urban area managed for amenity.

Pasture-woodland
Woodland in which grazing and browsing by animals is an important influence.

Pioneer species
A tree or shrub species capable of first colonising open ground, before other slower-growing species can become established.

Plantation
An area of woodland or forest consisting mainly of trees planted for timber.

Planting year
The year in which a planted tree crop first grew. For example, trees planted in autumn 00 or spring 01 would both be recorded as 01.

Pole stage
The stage between the thicket stage and maturity, when the young trees resemble poles. For broadleaves, this is from first thinning to about 50 years.

Pollard
A tree which is cut at 2-4m (6-12ft) above ground level, then left to grow again to produce a crop of branches. (v) To cut the branches from such a tree so that they will regrow.

Primary woodland
Woodland that has had a continuous cover of native trees throughout its history.

Provenance
The place of origin of a tree stock, which remains the same no matter where later generations of the tree are raised.

Pruning
Cutting branches from a standing tree.

Recalcitrant seed
Tree seed which cannot be partially dried for storage.

Recent woodland
Woodland which has grown up since the year 1600AD.

Respace
To cut out surplus young trees before they have reached the thinning stage. Refers in particular to naturally regenerated trees.

Ride
A permanent unsurfaced route within a woodland, used for access, demarcation, extraction of timber and shooting purposes.

Ring-barking
Damage to a tree due to the bark being removed from around the entire circumference of the stem.

Root collar
The base of the stem, where it joins the root.

Root/shoot ratio
The ratio of root growth to the branches and other aerial parts of a plant.

Rotation
The number of years from planting to felling of a tree crop; the length of time between successive cuttings of a coppice plot.

Sapwood
Wood which carries sap. In a young stem, this may be all of the wood; in a larger, older tree or branch, the outermost layer.

Scarifying
Disturbing the soil surface, typically to encourage germination of tree seed.

Screefing
Scraping away the surface vegetation prior to planting, to reduce initial weed competition.

Scrub
In ecology, an area dominated by shrubs, sometimes as a stage in succession to high forest. In forestry, an area of unproductive woodland.

Secondary woodland
Woodland growing on a site that has been cleared at some point in time.

Seedling
Refers to a plant raised from seed (rather than from vegetative propagation) while it remains in its original seedbed. After planting elsewhere, it is known as a transplant.

Semi-natural woodland
On ancient sites, woods made up mainly of native species growing where their presence is apparently natural and which have not obviously been planted. On recent sites, all stands that have originated mainly by natural regeneration.

Sets
Woody shoots of willow and poplar which root easily when inserted into the soil.

Short rotation coppice
A modern management system, using fast growing species such as willow and poplar, planted close together and cut on a three to five year rotation to produce wood chips.

Shrub layer
That part of the woodland structure, from about 2-4.5m (6-15ft) above ground containing shrubs and young growth of canopy trees.

Singling

Cutting out all but one to three stems on a coppice stool so that it will grow into a timber tree. Singled stems are known as 'stores', to distinguish them from 'maiden' trees, that have never been cut.

Softwood

The timber of a coniferous tree.

Spinney

A small wood or thicket, typically of spiny trees such as hawthorn and blackthorn.

Spot weeding

Weedkilling a spot around each tree, rather than along complete rows.

Stag-headed

Trees with dead branches which protrude from the top of a live crown. Usually the result of old age, but may also result from injury. Also commonly caused by agricultural drainage or other factors lowering the water table.

Stand

A group or area of trees.

Standard

In woodland structure, a tree forming the dominant layer of the canopy. In nursery stock, a tree with 1.8m (6ft) or more of clear stem.

Stem

The living trunk of a shrub or tree.

Stool

The stump or cut base of a shrub or tree from which new shoots grow.

Stooling

A method of propagating coppice in which regrowth from stools is earthed over to root and later cut away for transplanting.

Structure

The pattern and shape of growth within a woodland, such as the height and density of crowns, position and size of glades, and shape and orientation of margins.

Succession

The process by which one community of plants gives way to another in a series from coloniser to climax.

Sucker

A young tree arising from the roots of an older tree.

Thicket stage

Stage after planting and before the pole stage, when young trees have grown up enough to form a dense thicket.

Thinning

Removal of selected trees from a crop to give the remainder more growing space. A tree so removed.

Timber

The trunks of trees of large enough diameter to be suitable for producing beams and planks (minimum dimensions 4.5m/12ft length, and 7cm /3in top diameter); a tree with such a trunk; the use made of such a trunk.

Transpiration

The process by which a plant loses some of the water it absorbs, to allow further absorption by the roots.

Transplant

Small tree less than 120cm (4ft) in height, which has been moved from one nursery bed to another to improve the development of the root system.

Treeshelter

A translucent plastic tube for newly planted trees that encourages faster growth, and guards against predators.

Undercut

In the nursery – an undercut tree is one which has had its roots severed to improve development without transplanting.
In felling – a cut made in the front of a tree to reduce the chance of splitting when felling.

Understorey tree

A tree, the crown of which is below that of the dominant trees in the canopy.

Underwood

Wood, whether growing or cut, or coppice poles, young suckers or occasionally, pollard poles.

Viable seed

Seed which is capable of germinating.

Whip

A transplant under about 100cm (3ft) high.

Windblow/windthrow

Trees uprooted either partially or wholly by the wind.

Wood

The part of the stem, inside the cambium, which support the tree, carries water to the crown and stores reserves of food over the winter. Also poles and branches of smaller diameter than timber.

Wood pasture

An area of scattered trees in grassland on which farm animals or deer graze.

Xylem

The woody vascular tissue of a plant which conducts water and mineral salts in the stems, roots and leaves, and supports the softer tissues.

Index